ROLEX
ROLEX.COM

HE MAKES
FORMULA ONE
HAPPEN
WITH ENERGY,
DRIVE AND VISION.
SO DO WE.

Bernie Ecclestone runs the world's most prestigious sport. One season, five continents, 12 teams and over half a billion fans worldwide. It means compromise is not an option, and it means that speed, teamwork and precision are essential. That's why the man at the top demands the best. And that's why he chose us to be the official logistics partner of F1, ensuring that the entire sport is delivered across the globe.

www.dhl-brandworld.com/F1

 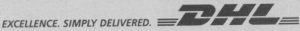

WILDLIFE AS CANON SEES IT

An invisible giant? Not quite, but the giant antpitta is heard much more than it is seen. It stays out of sight in dark, dense undergrowth, where pairs go their separate ways to forage but remain within earshot of each other. In addition to its calls, the antpitta is capable of singing 60-100 notes over a span of just four to six seconds, and the male's song advertises his fitness as a mate while warding off intruders to his territory. The virtuoso singer isn't much at flying, however, and sticks near the forest floor to probe the soft earth for food. But with its habitat being eaten up by deforestation, the antpitta is in real danger of disappearing forever.

As we see it, we can help make the world a better place. Raising awareness of endangered species is just one of the ways we at Canon are taking action—for the good of the planet we call home. Visit **canon.com/environment** to learn more.

NATIONAL GEOGRAPHIC

NOVEMBER 2010 · VOL. 218 · NO. 5

Blood drips
from her lips as
she squats to
give birth. That's
the duality of
Tlaltecuhtli, Aztec
earth goddess.
No one knows
what happened
to the 12-ton
monolith's midriff.
Story on page 110.
KENNETH GARRETT

OFFICIAL JOURNAL OF THE NATIONAL GEOGRAPHIC SOCIETY

NATIONAL GEOGRAPHIC

DEPARTMENTS

ngm.com

↖ **Pictures to Puzzle Out**
Each day you send us
thousands of Your Shot
photos. We pick and post
a daily dozen of the best.
See each one appear as
its own jigsaw—and see
how fast you can solve it.

EGILL BJARNASON

On the Cover
Wildebeests kick up dust as they
barrel across Liuwa Plain National
Park in Zambia at sunset.
Photo by Chris Johns

FOR SUBSCRIPTIONS, GIFT MEMBERSHIPS, OR CHANGES OF ADDRESS,
CONTACT CUSTOMER SERVICE AT *NGMSERVICE.COM*, OR CALL 1-800-NGS-LINE
(647-5463). OUTSIDE THE U.S. AND CANADA PLEASE CALL +1-813-979-6845.

Smart meters for a smarter planet.

Blackouts. Power cuts. Economic recovery at risk. The prospect of not having enough energy to go round is unthinkable. Yet if the UK continues to use energy at the current rate, demand could outstrip supply as early as 2016.

Clearly we have to develop new energy sources, but increasing supply is only part of the equation. A more immediate and cost-effective strategy is to encourage consumers to use less, particularly at times when energy is most expensive to supply. This would also help the energy industry reduce its emissions.

Simply increasing the price of power is unlikely to reduce consumption, but fortunately there is another option. As our world gets more intelligent, interconnected and instrumented, smart meters can give consumers better information about their energy use and its cost, encouraging them to change when and how they use power.

They also give suppliers a way to develop intelligent time-of-use tariffs that encourage customers to delay consumption until demand is low and costs fall. This can help cut energy bills, lessen the likelihood of power cuts, and reduce greenhouse gas emissions – a fantastic win-win-win scenario.

In Holland, IBM works with energy company Nuon on just such a project. In a pilot test of smart meter-based energy management systems in 500 households, energy use is monitored, targets set and usage patterns influenced by various beyond-the-meter-services. The next phase of the pilot will also include switching off unnecessary appliances. Anticipated savings average 14% on electricity and 9% on gas – that's around £200 a year for an average household. In another study, participants who responded to real-time prices reduced peak power use by 15%.

The technology for nationwide energy monitoring already exists. When the UK government asked energy consultants Hildebrand to scale up its energy monitoring solution for all UK homes, they worked with IBM's software laboratory near Winchester. Together they created a solution that can collect, store and analyse huge volumes of data – 50,000 data points per second – making it scalable to millions of homes. This enables real-time analysis and optimisation of electricity usage for households – a vital step in making our energy system smarter.

Developments like these will become increasingly important as smart meters and smart grids start to transform the way we supply and use energy. So let's do it. Let's build a smarter planet.

ibm.com/smarterplanet/uk/metering

EDITOR'S NOTE

Cape buffalo
on the move
in Botswana's
Okavango Delta
play a vital role
in the region's
ecosystem.

I awoke at sunrise to a day on the Serengeti Plain that scarcely
resembled the peaceful night before. The landscape that had been so quiet and
empty was filled with thousands of wildebeests. They had followed the rain in
search of grass, but this hardly seemed like an organized migration. It was anarchy
in motion; wildebeests bucked and staggered in tight circles. They are comical-
looking animals. African folklore says they were made from spare parts left from
the creation of other beasts, but their role in sustaining the Serengeti is serious.
Their migratory patterns are critical.

Bison once played a similar role on the North American prairie. In 1806 William
Clark wrote: "I assended to the high Country and from an eminance I had a view
of…a greater number of buffalow than I had ever seen before at one time. I must
have seen near 20,000 of those animals feeding on this plain." When Clark journeyed
west with Meriwether Lewis, tens of millions of bison lived on the grasslands,
shaping vegetation, dispersing seeds, coexisting with burrowing owls and prairie
dogs. By the late 1800s bison had been hunted nearly to extinction.

Fortunately, many other migratory spectacles survive. This month the world of
migrations comes to life on the pages of our magazine, on the National Geographic
Channel, and at *nationalgeographic.com*. Our photographers and writers spent two
years on the project. They were astonished and inspired by the determination and
grace of these animals. I am sure you will be too.

Chris Johns

▲
Mt. Emei waterfall.

Shot using the Samsung NX10
with 18-55mm lens, f/22,
ISO 400, 4 exposure.

**TYRONE
TURNER**

Tyrone Turner is a photojournalist
based in Arlington, Virginia. His
assignments have taken him from
Brazil to Baghdad to the bayous
of Louisiana with his camera
in hand. In addition to his work
for *National Geographic*, Turner
has produced award-winning
photographs for national and
international publications such as
*Time, Newsweek, U.S. News and
World Report*, and the
Los Angeles Times.

Photography Flows on China's Sacred Mountain

There is an abundance of beauty on the slopes of Mt. Emei, in the Sichuan Province of
Western China. Much of this beauty comes from the many Buddhist temples that dot its
slopes, making the mountain a popular destination for pilgrims of all ages.

It is the facet of Emei's natural beauty, however, that *National Geographic* photographer
Tyrone Turner was moved to capture—resulting in the almost surreal image you see above.

Turner describes: "It was taken at the end of a hike down Mt. Emei. Discovering this scene,
I knew that I wanted to shoot it with a long exposure so that the water would flow through
the bottom of the image, framed by the boulders."

Having come upon such an opportunity, he wasted no time: "I hopped over the railing,
scrambled into the water, and set up the camera on a tripod in the stream. The convenient
size of the NX10 made it all so easy; it's a camera that doesn't get in the way, wherever you
need to go to get your shot."

Not only did the AMOLED help him perfectly frame the scene, but the multi-exposure
settings lent the water a luminous quality. Turner says: "Thanks to its large APS-C sensor,
the NX10 gives me the supreme picture quality I need."

NX10

www.samsung.com
www.samsungimaging.com

SAMSUNG

TURN ON TOMORROW

NATIONAL GEOGRAPHIC

Inspiring people to care about the planet

The National Geographic Society is chartered in Washington, D.C., as a nonprofit scientific and educational organization "for the increase and diffusion of geographic knowledge." Since 1888 the Society has supported more than 9,000 explorations and research projects, adding to knowledge of earth, sea, and sky.

YOUR BOARDING PASS IS RINGING.

It's your contacts, emails, diary, music library, photo album, access to the world. We know your mobile phone is your life. That's why you can now use it as your boarding pass.

 We know why you fly° AmericanAirlines°

AA.com

LETTERS

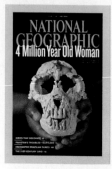

July 2010

Evolutionary Road

The title on the July 2010 cover reading "4-Million-Year-Old Woman" was a bit sensational and even misleading. A less interesting but more accurate title would have been "4-Million-Year-Old Female Hominid." The term "woman" refers to our own species and not to females of other species.

BRIAN RITTER
Huntington Beach, California

This article is the best description of human evolution that I have ever read. Besides being understandable to a layperson (me), it illustrates the diligent work and dedication of the many archaeologists, paleontologists, and geologists who have devoted their lives and talents to this study. This article should elicit many responses from the creationists. Please publish some of these letters.

RICHARD D. STACY
Montrose, Colorado

I thought you might find it interesting to see that your printer has messed up the July issue. Imagine my surprise when I cracked it open only to find the inside has articles from *Evolution Today* magazine. I was crestfallen as I discovered that my joyful romp through wonderful lands to learn about other people and places had been replaced by a scientific treatise. I can only hope that next month the printer corrects the error so that I can resume reading the material I was interested in when I paid for my subscription.

DAVE BUEHLER
Shoreline, Washington

Bowerbirds

It took me a long time to get past the second page because I was deciding which bower I would have chosen! I wasn't even aware that I was doing it until I decided: bower #1 on page 70, for sure. It won on its symmetry and color scheme. I am also pretty sure that if my husband were a bowerbird, his bower would have been #4 on page 71—which would not even have been in the running.

SUSAN DYRUD MacDONALD
Plymouth, Minnesota

I think the first time that I laughed out loud at a *National Geographic* photo was in the "Animals at Play" article from December 1994. The second time was seeing the confounded-looking bowerbird holding the pink paper clip.

MATT JUDGE
Indianapolis, Indiana

The 21st-Century Grid

Your article about the grid did not mention the linemen that keep the grid up and running. As a lineman's wife, I know firsthand the part these men and women play in the construction, upkeep, and repair of the grid. From transmission lines to distribution lines, without linemen, make no mistake, there would be no grid. The function of a lineman used to be recognized as a valuable part of society. Glen Campbell romanticized it in the song "Wichita Lineman," and the book about a lineman's life, *Slim*, was made into a movie. However, this acknowledgment seems to have gone by the wayside. I fear the very idea of such a technologically complicated and vastly modern new grid has led us to forget the men and women who use hard work and know-how to keep the electricity flowing.

NANCI LEICHING
Somers, Connecticut

You might have mentioned the grid's vulnerability to an electromagnetic pulse (EMP) attack. An EMP is a high-energy magnetic wave that is created upon detonating a nuclear device. A high-altitude nuclear detonation destroys sensitive electrical equipment over a wide area. This would include computers that control the grid—many are not shielded for such an event. Military experts testifying to the U.S. Congress on this issue warned that as more rogue nations obtain nuclear capability, the United States becomes more vulnerable to attack. This could cause a cascade failure across the United States, which would be an infrastructure disaster.

GREGORY L. SMITH
Chatham, New Jersey

Contact Us

Email ngsforum@ngm.com
Write National Geographic Magazine, PO Box 98199, Washington, DC 20090-8199. Include name, address, and daytime telephone. Letters may be edited for clarity and length.

LETTERS

A key fact was left out of the story. Study after study shows that our current grid can easily accommodate 20 percent or more of wind and solar power. While you label wind and solar as "intermittent," you explain how the largest blackout in the U.S. was caused by existing fossil fuel and nuclear plants but somehow fail to apply the label of intermittent to these plants. The grid has always dealt with intermittence, both on the generating and the demand sides, although getting to 100 percent renewable energy will indeed require some additional storage capacity.

You also say that coal-fired electricity costs a few cents a kilowatt-hour, while renewables are substantially more. Old coal-fired power plants without air pollution control devices did generate electricity at between 2.5 to 3.5 cents in the past. However, new state and federal regulations make coal-fired plants more expensive than wind power and even solar when you truly consider the value of solar—such as the ability to site it at the point of demand so that you don't need new transmission.

ROBERT UKEILEY
Berea, Kentucky

Based on a report I heard, U.S. power-production efficiency has not improved since the days of the Eisenhower Administration. That is simply deplorable. If the expanding electricity grid is to function properly, new efficiencies should be mandatory.

M. VINCENT TURNER
Bristol, Connecticut

I agree that we need to upgrade our electrical grid with better, more efficient technology. But it's concerning that we're focusing on green energy when it doesn't seem nearly as efficient as coal, nuclear, or hydroelectric power. I'm not against wind or solar, but they're not the answer to our energy needs—they're just a piece of the overall picture.

JEREMY BUNDGARD
Minneapolis, Minnesota

> I agree that we need to upgrade our electrical grid with better, more efficient technology. But it's concerning that we're focusing on green energy when it doesn't seem nearly as efficient as coal, nuclear, or hydroelectric power.

I was surprised that no mention was made of the pioneering work of Nikola Tesla, who is the father of high-voltage AC power transmission. Edison's low-voltage DC distribution system was a technological dead end. Tesla invented the high-voltage polyphase AC power system that the modern high-voltage DC power transmission systems are now based upon. Tesla also discovered the principle of the rotating magnetic field. This led to the patenting of the ubiquitous AC induction motor, which drives most of the rotating loads of industrial and domestic appliances. Together these form a large part of the grid's load. It is very sad that Tesla is now almost forgotten in the public mind.

RON BARNES
King's Lynn, England

I was appalled that you would publish an article that refers to the vulnerability of our electric power grid, and then include a detailed map of the grid, showing all the distribution lines and generating routing centers. Could you have made it any easier for those who would do us harm?

GEORGE McPHETERS
Burlington, North Carolina

Pakistan's Heartland
John Lancaster's article described Pakistan's rich historical past, reflecting multicultural influences rooted in an atmosphere of tolerance and positive development. However, there was essentially no focus on the nature and identity of the threat, the Taliban. The viciousness of the Taliban toward Pakistan's sovereignty was described in such neutral terms that the reader might think that the threat was about as serious as the common cold. An opportunity to disclose the impact of the Taliban and its potential destruction of all that is good in Pakistan was lost. In sharp contrast there was no attempt to attenuate the anti-American feelings expressed by students at the madrassa in Bahawalpur, many of whom will embark on a course of jihad, fighting, and killing following graduation. Is there any pro-American feeling in Pakistan? Not according to this one-sided article.

ROBERT B. REDDEN
North Falmouth, Massachusetts

There's something inside
CARLO DALLA CHIESA

#9 ANGELICA FROM SAXONY

GRAINS OF PARADISE FROM WEST AFRICA

BOMBAYSAPPHIRE.COM/INSIDE

There's something inside
The
BOMBAY SAPPHIRE

Enjoy Bombay Sapphire Responsibly.
for the facts **drinkaware.co.uk**

LETTERS

The Big Idea: Space Trash

I'm reading back issues of *National Geographic* and had just finished the September 1957 issue when I picked up the July 2010 issue from my mailbox. The space-trash article shows the oldest orbital debris to be the Vanguard I satellite launched in 1958. I believe that's the same satellite touted as a "new moon" in an IBM ad mentioning the Vanguard Computing Center on page 437 of the September 1957 issue.

BILL NORTON
St. Paul, Minnesota

Health: Pomegranates Packing a Punch

The medicinal power of pomegranate rind has been made use of in India from time immemorial. The rind is saved and sun dried. For any kind of stomach ailment, boil a couple of pieces of the dried rind in water and drink it warm or cold. It arrests the stomach complaint with surprising speed. It is used in many Ayurvedic medicinal preparations too.

ELSY SATHEESAN
Charlottesville, Virginia

Regarding the potential health benefits of pomegranate, the head researcher muses: "We don't think it would have major side effects, because we've looked to nature to show the way." While the study seems promising, nature is not as benign as generally believed. A case in point is the fatal kidney disease and urothelial cancer associated with use of an herbal diet aid containing a natural aristolochic acid. This was first observed in Belgium in the early 1990s. Remember that chemical toxicity isn't limited to synthetic chemicals.

The list of natural poisons is long and growing.

GORDON GRIBBLE
Hanover, New Hampshire

Conservation: Ox Redux

The fast-food industry, where size does matter, must have taken note of Project Tauros's aim to bring back the auroch. That much beef on the hoof equals a lot of burgers. We saved the North American bison from extinction; now the meat is found in every supermarket. It is somehow sad that we must resurrect an extinct species to feed our insatiable appetites. What's next—Kentucky fried passenger pigeon?

JOHN H. COBB, JR.
Roswell, Georgia

> Then he picked up a two-by-four, and as he held it, arms extended above his head, it burst into flames. Here, I thought, is a man with a death wish. Today George is 95 and healthy, living in Irvine, California.

Geography: Don't Walk in Memphis

When I saw your story on the study of dangerous cities for pedestrians, I immediately recognized a correlation among the low-risk cities marked on your accompanying map: Most of the safest pedestrian cities rank high in *Bicycling* magazine's 2010 rankings of the best cities for cycling. In fact, six of the top ten bike cities rank in the lowest 25 percent of dangerous pedestrian cities—and *Bicycling*'s #1 pick, Minneapolis, ranked last out of the 52 cities rated for pedestrian fatalities.

DAVE VANDERWIEL
Brecksville, Ohio

The title "Don't Walk in Memphis" was misleading. I'm guessing it was an attempt at humor. Memphis was only mentioned as an also-ran problem city. It was not atop the list. There were no statistics about the dangers of walking in Memphis. As a lifelong resident of Memphis and its suburbs, I was upset to see an exaggerated negative reference without justification. The city gets enough bad press as it is.

JOHN STACY
Olive Branch, Mississippi

The title was intended to reference the popular song "Walking in Memphis." We meant no disrespect to your hometown.

Flashback

Thirty years before George Speake (seen in the July Flashback) became my father-in-law, I saw him do the lightning-from-his-fingers stunt and thought he was crazy. Then he picked up a two-by-four, and as he held it, arms extended above his head, it burst into flames. Here, I thought, is a man with a death wish. Today George is 95 and healthy, living in Irvine, California. He is still up to some old tricks and full of spark.

KAREN BURKLAND
Sherman Oaks, California

CUT FUEL COSTS
WITH MICHELIN TYRES*.

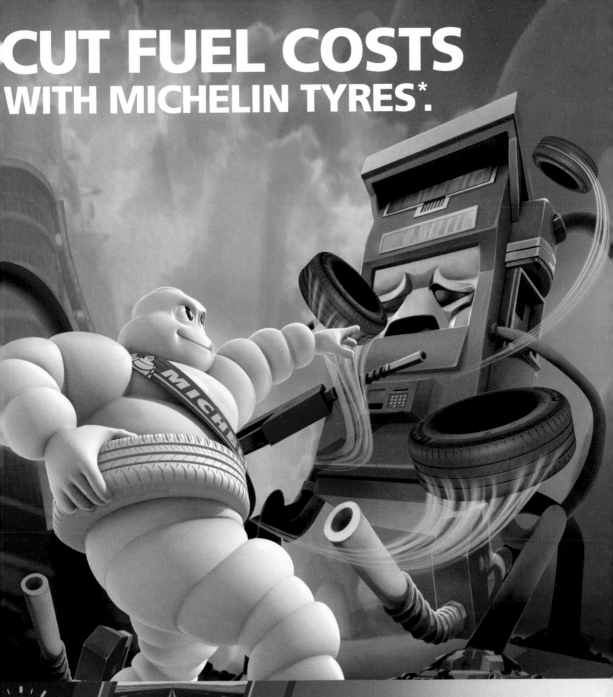

There are important reasons to choose
a MICHELIN ENERGY™ Saver tyre:

STOPPING DISTANCE	TYRE LIFE	FUEL EFFICIENCY
STOPS UP TO **3 METRES** SHORTER ON WET ROADS***	LASTS **6,000 MILES** LONGER THAN ITS COMPETITORS**	SAVES UP TO **80 LITRES** OF FUEL*

The MICHELIN ENERGY™ Saver tyre is strong on fuel efficiency and can help save up to 80 litres of fuel*. Not only that, it lasts 6,000 miles longer than its competitors** and can reduce braking distance by up to 3 metres in wet conditions***.

See how the right tyre changes everything at **www.michelin.co.uk**

*Estimate of average saving with MICHELIN ENERGY™ Saver tyres compared to main competitors for petrol vehicles. TÜV SÜD Automotive 2009 rolling resistance tests on 15 key sizes for the European market (Michelin was first in 13 sizes and second in 2 sizes). Calculated over the average life span for MICHELIN tyres i.e. 28,000 miles (internal source).

**On average for the MICHELIN ENERGY™ Saver tyre compared to its main competitors. Tests conducted by TÜV SÜD Automotive in 2008, 2009, 2010 on tyre sizes 175/65 R 14 T, 195/65 R 15 H and 205/55 R 16 V with tyres available on the market at the time.

***Compared to the previous generation of the MICHELIN ENERGY™ Saver tyre. 2007 TÜV SÜD Automotive test on tyre size 175/65 R 14 T.

Vibrancy and Variety
The world is alive with colors and textures, shapes and perspectives. Your photos are too. In fact, the best ones document diversity—poignant tableaux, landscape panoramas, and so much more. So keep that in mind, and keep sending us your best. Every month this page features two photographs: one chosen by our editors, one chosen by our readers via online voting. For more information, go to *ngm.com/yourshot*.

EDITORS' CHOICE

Paul Cotter Charlotte, North Carolina

As his mother's health declined, Cotter, 52, thought "of all her small acts of kindness—like the tomato soup she made for me when I was a little boy." This shot was his way to say "farewell and to thank her for warming my heart."

Navid Baraty Brooklyn, New York

Most evenings San Francisco's Ocean Beach is foggy, cold, and empty. But last fall Baraty, 29, caught this sunset sight: a "multitude of little silhouettes on the glistening sand with mist encroaching."

READERS' CHOICE

THAI

50th
ANNIVERSARY
1960-2010

Escape East or Down Under.
THAI can take you there.

THAI takes you to the best of Asia, Australia and New Zealand.

The endless sights of Asia and the wonderland of Oceania are all yours to explore, or any of
our destinations across 5 continents. For business or leisure, earn miles on
Royal Orchid Plus as you discover a world that's smooth as silk on THAI.

Scotland Peering through glass, visitors at the Edinburgh Zoo regard—and are regarded by—Tibor, a Sumatran tiger. The three-year-old male was born in captivity. About 400 of this subspecies, the world's smallest tiger, live in the wild.

PHOTO: DAVID CHESKIN, PRESS ASSOCIATION/AP IMAGES

Kenya Aimed skyward from photos atop a train, the eyes of women pierce a rooftop landscape in Nairobi's Kibera slum. The display, part of a global art project, paid tribute to women from Africa, Brazil, India, and Cambodia.

United States A 14-week-old male fawn gazes out a window at the Sarvey Wildlife Care Center. The Arlington, Washington, facility rehabs regional animals, including up to 30 orphaned or injured young deer each spring.

PHOTO: ANNIE MARIE MUSSELMAN

EXPERT'S EYE
NATURE

PHOTO TIPS

- Be curious and read extensively: know rivers and seas, and the creatures that inhabit them.
- Check out tidal pools, ponds, freshwater lakes. Dynamic, original photos may be close to home.
- Study what's already been shot underwater. Know the clichés and try something original.
- Have at least 100 dives under your belt before taking a camera.
- Become a swimming studio. Experiment with strobes. Find your subject, then add light to the moment.

David Doubilet's underwater photography has graced the pages of *National Geographic* for four decades and brought readers face-to-face with a diversity of sea creatures, from sharks to clownfish. Whatever his subject, he tries to bring intimacy and depth to the task of illuminating aquatic life.

"It's not enough to let a fish parade in front of your camera and capture it in that split second," says the photographer. "A good nature photo must be intimate and vibrant; it should capture the texture of that fish and its habitat, the curtain of life upon which it parades."

The photographer who approaches the subject with respect and care will be rewarded, according to Doubilet. When he photographed these South Australian sea lions on their grassy carpet near Little Hopkins Island, the creatures responded to his non-intrusive presence by gently tickling his hands with their whiskers—a warm moment in a cold ocean.

To find out more about David Doubilet, go to:

http://www.daviddoubilet.com/

Reveal your natural talent with the National Geographic International Photography Contest

Islay presents many views to a photographer. The light and even the landscape seem to change from moment to moment, it is this environment that shapes the character of our perfectly balanced Bowmore Single Malt Whisky. With a passion for photography and with nature at our core, we invite you to capture moments at their finest.

We're delighted to partner with National Geographic UK in 2010 and have been calling on you to get to the core of photography, by entering the International Photography Contest 2010. Time is running out to enter your photographs, with the contest coming to a close 31st October, for the chance to feature in a Bowmore advert in National Geographic and to win a truly magical trip to the home of Bowmore - the Scottish island of Islay. To make more of your photography, visit us at Bowmore.com for hints and tips from expert photographers. Good luck, or as we would say in Scot's Gaelic - g'un rob h math agad.

VISIT NATIONALGEOGRAPHIC.COM/IPCUK2010 TO ENTER

NATIONAL GEOGRAPHIC
INTERNATIONAL
PHOTOGRAPHY CONTEST 2010

IN PARTNERSHIP WITH

BOWMORE
ISLAY
SINGLE MALT
SCOTCH WHISKY

ISLAY TO THE CORE

VISIT BOWMORE.COM FOR MORE
drinkaware.co.uk for the facts

THE FIRST ISLAY SINGLE MALT WHISKY SINCE 1779

Mallard photograph by Nigel Hillier, IPC 2009

CONSERVATION

Tracking Gorillas When counting mountain gorillas, try to avoid the animals themselves. That's the tack primatologist Martha Robbins and 71 others took while conducting their latest census of the endangered species. "We don't want to encounter unhabituated gorillas," she explains, "because it is stressful for them." Rather than seeking out individuals, the team followed clues such as dung, nests, and trails to estimate gorilla numbers in the volcanic Virunga Mountains of equatorial Africa—one of only two places where the great apes live.

At last count, in 2006, some 680 were estimated to remain in that area and Uganda's Bwindi Impenetrable National Park. The 2010 Virunga census, followed by a Bwindi survey next year, will tell how the gorillas are faring now, after years of poaching, deforestation, and political unrest. Also expected, thanks to fecal-sample analysis: fresh insights into the elusive creatures' genetic diversity and overall health. —*Catherine Barker*

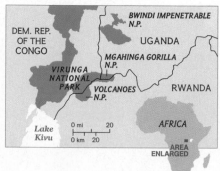

The Virunga range is home to one of just two mountain gorilla populations that remain today.

In Rwanda's Volcanoes National Park, a young silverback sits in solitude.

When David Jewitt was on life support, his wife needed our support as well.

When David Jewitt suffered a stroke, his wife knew they had insurance, but had no idea how to make a claim.

Still in a state of shock, she called Aviva, where she spoke to advisor Mike Matwiejczyk. The first thing Mike did was simply to talk through the situation. Then he started to sort her practical problems.

At Aviva, we believe that insurance isn't just a financial business. It's a service that people call on at some of the most difficult moments in their life.

Maybe it's because we try to treat our customers this way that we have so many of them – more than 53 million, in 28 countries.

youarethebigpicture.com

AVIVA

| Retirement | Investments | Insurance | Health |

We have 53 million customers in 28 countries.

But that's only part of the picture.

OCEANS

830 miles above Earth
The TOPEX/Poseidon satellite begins mapping the surface of the sea.

MILESTONES IN OCEAN EXPLORATION

1913   1934   1943   1960 1965   1977   1985   1992   2010

Sea surface
Acoustic exploration of the ocean starts when Reginald Fessenden tests an oscillator that will be used to locate icebergs.

5,000 ft

210 feet
Jacques Cousteau and Émile Gagnan develop and test modern scuba.

205 feet
Sealab II, an underwater habitat, is lowered off the coast of California.

3,028 feet
Manned exploration of the deep begins in earnest when William Beebe and Otis Barton are lowered in a tethered bathysphere.

10,000

8,000 feet
Hydrothermal vents and chemosynthetic animals are discovered in the Galápagos Rift.

15,000

12,600 feet
Robert Ballard, later a Hubbard Medal winner, and his team find the wreck of the *Titanic*.

16,000 feet and above
The decade-long Census of Marine Life unveils hundreds of new species.

20,000

25,000

30,000

35,800 feet
Co-piloted by Don Walsh and Jacques Piccard, the *Trieste* reaches the bottom of the ocean—the Pacific's Mariana Trench.

35,000

A Century Beneath the Sea

In 1960 a bathyscaphe took two men to the deepest point on Earth. In 2010 that manned descent to the Mariana Trench—still unmatched—won co-pilot Don Walsh the Hubbard Medal, National Geographic's top honor for research and discovery. Yet it remains just a single, vital drop in an age of ocean exploration.

The secrets of the deep have emerged from research done far below the waves—and from far above them. Oceanographer Walter Munk deems the satellite TOPEX/Poseidon's 13-year mapping of the sea surface, showing how currents affect climate, "the most successful ocean experiment of all times."

What will the next century of marine science reveal? Maritime historian Helen Rozwadowski says that although most scientists think robotics are the way forward, some idealists still call for a Sealab-style colonization of the sea. Either way, she says, environmental concerns will likely influence all future ocean exploration—"unless somehow the dreamers get our attention again." —*Jeremy Berlin*

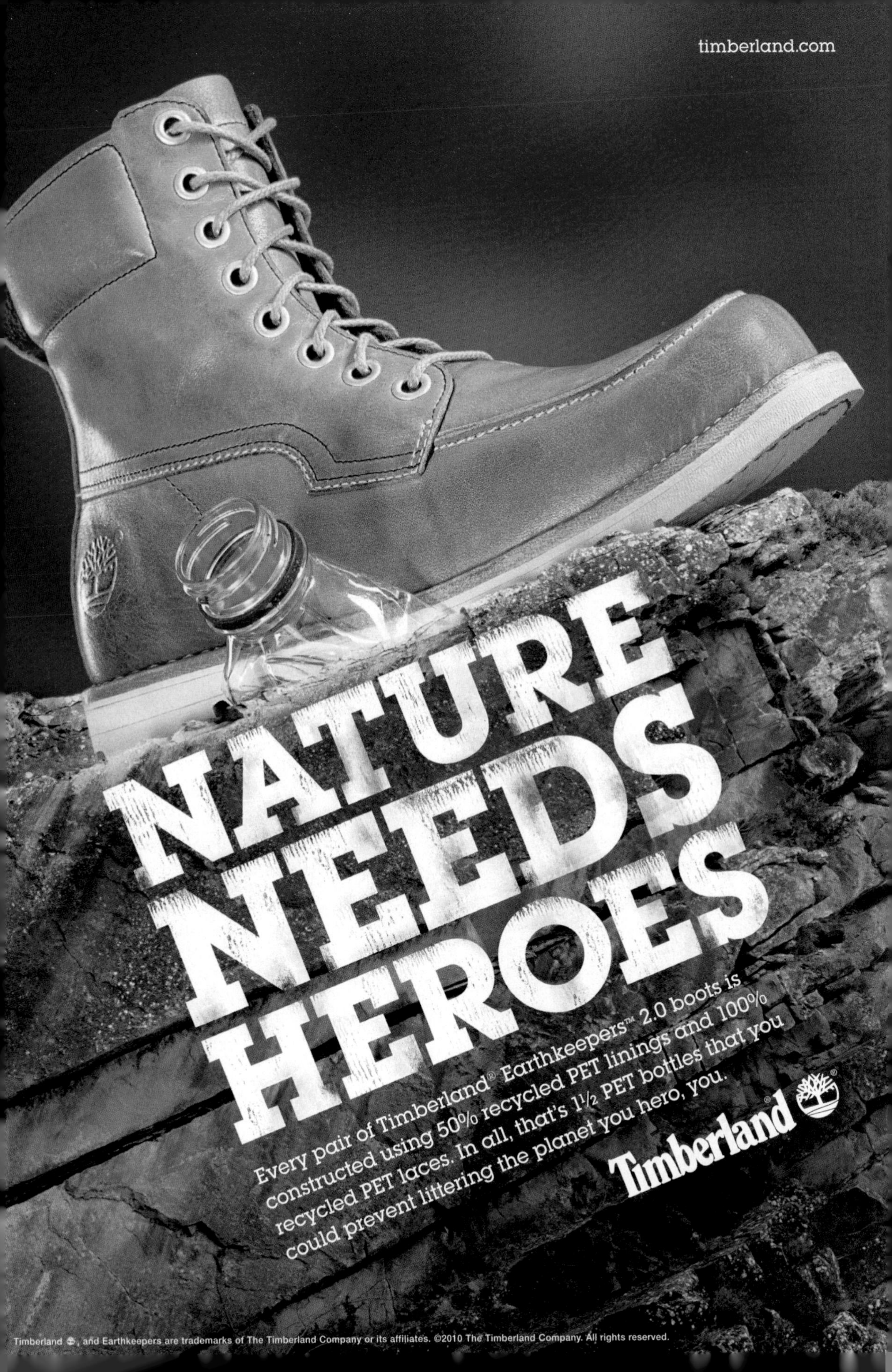

timberland.com
NATURE
NEEDS
HEROES
Every pair of Timberland® Earthkeepers™ 2.0 boots is constructed using 50% recycled PET linings and 100% recycled PET laces. In all, that's 1½ PET bottles that you could prevent littering the planet you hero, you.
Timberland®
Timberland, and Earthkeepers are trademarks of The Timberland Company or its affiliates. ©2010 The Timberland Company. All rights reserved.

Liyakot Ali, 13, makes cooking pots in a Bangladesh factory.

No Minor Issue

Across the globe, kids can be seen hawking trinkets and swabbing down tea shops. But these are only the most visible of the world's 215 million child laborers. A new report by the United Nations' International Labour Organization (ILO) says that 60 percent of them toil unseen in the agricultural sector, often for little or no pay. And the isolation of those in domestic work, says Human Rights Watch, can increase the odds of their exploitation.

Between 2004 and 2008 the number of child laborers decreased by seven million; Asia and Latin America, particularly Brazil, led the way, thanks to government initiatives. Yet South Asia

remains home to the most in the world; one in four sub-Saharan kids is still classified as a child laborer; and the economic crisis could stall progress by feeding demand for cheap labor.

Going forward, the ILO urges a global commitment to compulsory education—by abolishing school fees, for instance—and government pacts with organized workers. It estimates that spending $140 billion in sub-Saharan Africa over 20 years could produce up to $724 billion in benefits, including massive health-care savings as children cease doing hazardous work. "The world can afford this," the report concludes. Call it a minor investment with a major payoff. —*Noy Thrupkaew*

Child labor estimates by region 2008

Child laborers include those under 12 doing any jobs other than household chores. Long hours, underground work, and heavy-machinery use are termed hazardous.

Asia; the Pacific*

Child laborers
114 million

Children in hazardous work
48 million

Sub-Saharan Africa

65 million

39 million

Latin America; the Caribbean

14 million

9 million

Other

22 million

19 million

*EXCLUDES AUSTRALIA, NEW ZEALAND, JAPAN, AND PARTS OF CENTRAL ASIA
PHOTO: G. M. B. AKASH, PANOS PICTURES. GRAPHIC: MINA LIU. SOURCE: INTERNATIONAL LABOUR ORGANIZATION

Also available at
John Lewis

Galehead Long Down jacket, filled with 800gm down fill for maximum insulation. Signature hard wearing Nailhead canvas - 60% organic cotton, 40% recycled polyester. Microporous backing repels water yet retains breathability.

Available at all Timberland stores including Westfield and Regent Street, London. Trafford Centre, Manchester. Find your nearest store at timberland.com

Medical marijuana like this is federally supplied to only a handful of patients.

Approval in the U.S. for medical marijuana 2010

■ In favor
■ Opposed
■ Don't know

A minimum of 61% of all groups are in favor.

Gender
Men   100%
Women

Ethnicity
White
Black
Hispanic

Age
18-29
30-49
50-64
65+

Education
College graduate
Some college
High school or less

Political affiliation
Republican
Democrat
Independent

Reefer Referral

Here's a sign that the times are a changin': Nearly three out of four Americans say they favor legalizing medical marijuana in their state, according to a 2010 Pew Research Center survey. And 41 percent think all marijuana should be legal, up from 35 percent in 2008 and 12 percent in a 1969 Gallup poll.

Pot has become political in recent years. This summer Congress let the District of Columbia join a dozen-plus states with medical-marijuana laws on the books. Proponents say legalization will create tax revenues and save money on enforcement. And the American College of Physicians and the American Medical Association have endorsed research on the plant's makeup. Issued for glaucoma and to help cancer patients deal with chemotherapy, cannabinoids like THC are also being probed for anticancer properties.

All of which means aging hippies aren't alone. The Pew poll found backing for medical marijuana across the political spectrum and all age groups—a clear sign that tolerance is growing. —*Alex Dominguez*

PHOTO: PAUL WELLMAN. CHART: LAWSON PARKER, NGM STAFF
SOURCE: PEW RESEARCH CENTER FOR THE PEOPLE & THE PRESS

1895-2010.
IT TAKES TIME TO ACHIEVE PERFECTION.

SEIKO

DEDICATED TO PERFECTION

ANANTA. In 1895, SEIKO crafted its first mechanical watch. For more than a century, we have built a tradition of continuous innovation that has enriched luxury watchmaking: the magic lever winding system in 1959, award-winning chronometers in the 1960's, the mechanical chronograph in 1969, the SPRON 510* alloy for the mainspring in 1997. Today, with a 45 hour power reserve, 34 jewels and a design inspired by Katana, the ancient Japanese art of sword making, Ananta renews this tradition.

seiko.co.uk

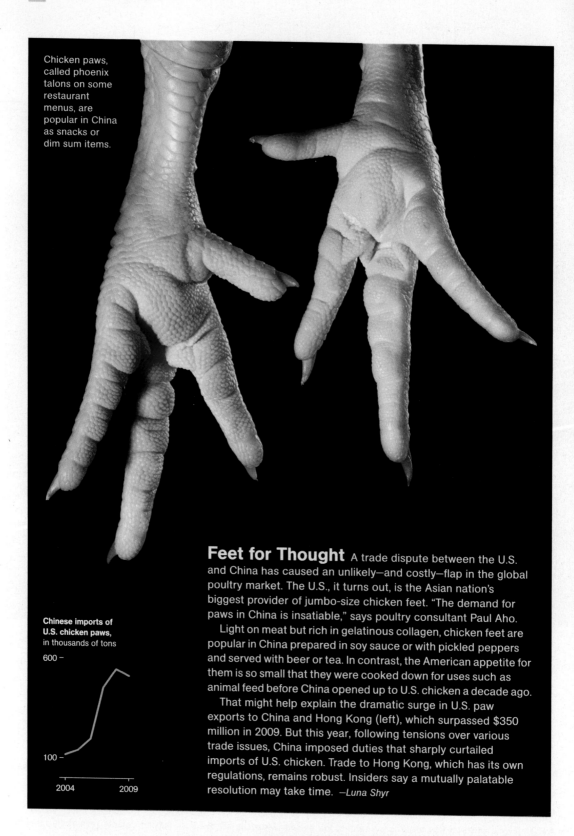

Chicken paws, called phoenix talons on some restaurant menus, are popular in China as snacks or dim sum items.

Chinese imports of U.S. chicken paws, in thousands of tons

600 –

100 –

2004   2009

Feet for Thought
A trade dispute between the U.S. and China has caused an unlikely—and costly—flap in the global poultry market. The U.S., it turns out, is the Asian nation's biggest provider of jumbo-size chicken feet. "The demand for paws in China is insatiable," says poultry consultant Paul Aho.

Light on meat but rich in gelatinous collagen, chicken feet are popular in China prepared in soy sauce or with pickled peppers and served with beer or tea. In contrast, the American appetite for them is so small that they were cooked down for uses such as animal feed before China opened up to U.S. chicken a decade ago.

That might help explain the dramatic surge in U.S. paw exports to China and Hong Kong (left), which surpassed $350 million in 2009. But this year, following tensions over various trade issues, China imposed duties that sharply curtailed imports of U.S. chicken. Trade to Hong Kong, which has its own regulations, remains robust. Insiders say a mutually palatable resolution may take time. —*Luna Shyr*

PHOTO: REBECCA HALE, NGM STAFF. CHART SOURCE: RICHARD LOBB, NATIONAL CHICKEN COUNCIL

Let the wind take you places
your imagination has not yet been.

Come knowing what you want to see.

And see what you do not know.

Lose track of days. Discover endless tranquility.

Take it all in. Through your eyes, your ears, your hands, your soul.

And leave with a new found sense of discovery.

Abu Dhabi. Travellers welcome.

Recommended as a Top 10 destination to visit this year by
Frommer's and Lonely Planet. **www.visitabudhabi.ae**

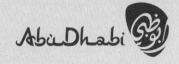

Maple Flow in Flux

The tapping of maple trees to make syrup is a rite of spring for a reason. Springtime brings cold nights followed by warm days, a combination that alternately freezes and thaws sap. That's when syrup producers drill small holes to capture the fluid as it drips out, ideally just before the sap is ready to flow.

Now climate change may be shrinking the critical "freeze-thaw" window and making its onset more difficult to predict, according to Tim Perkins of the University of Vermont's Proctor Maple Research Center. In the New England–New York region, the main U.S. producer of maple syrup, the sugaring season has shrunk by 3.2 days, or 10 percent, in 40 years, and now starts some eight days earlier on average. Shifting temperatures affect sap flow—about 40 gallons of sap are boiled down to make one gallon of syrup—and can disrupt the timing of tapping.

Fortunately, vacuum pumps that help draw out sap can offset potential losses in yield. As for the seasonal data, some syrup makers are taking the variability in stride. Says Dana Wildes, whose family has produced maple syrup on its Vermont farm for more than four decades, "We go through cycles, and we're in a cycle." —*Luna Shyr*

Length of Massachusetts maple-sugaring season

— 45 days

35 days

30 days

— 25

1963   2003

PHOTO: REBECCA HALE, NGM STAFF. CHART SOURCES: NATIONAL AGRICULTURAL STATISTICS SERVICE, USDA; PROCTOR MAPLE RESEARCH CENTER, UNIVERSITY OF VERMONT

All the best things on screen start with great writing.

Join the new Times and Sunday Times websites now and discover what happens when quality journalism meets the latest technology.
Just £1 for your first 30 days.

- Go quickly to the heart of issues with breaking news, incisive summaries and email alerts from our award winning journalists

- Your favourite sections and writers brought vividly to life through unique features like the Review Booth and our stunning interactive graphics

- Enjoy daily lunchtime debates and live Q&As with key personalities – and join in if you want to

- Plus, this month watch out for exclusive arts coverage from celebrity contributor Rupert Everett

Our two exciting new websites are yours for just £1 for the first 30 days. Subscribe now.

thetimes.co.uk

thesundaytimes.co.uk

THE TIMES
THE SUNDAY TIMES

ARCHAEOLOGY

Easter Island Hats For centuries visitors have marveled at the mysteries of Easter Island's 800-plus *moai,* colossal human figures carved of stone to represent ancestors. Equally puzzling are the red "hats" atop some statues—which 18th-century European explorers barely had time to admire before their own hats were brazenly stolen by islanders they met.

Why the local fascination with headgear? Ancient Polynesians associated it with high status, so the moai's cylindrical *pukao* likely signified certain statues' importance. But how did multi-ton rounds of red scoria, a volcanic rock quarried up to eight miles from the moai, come to rest on these giant heads? The hats were apparently rolled to their destinations, and some experts believe they were maneuvered up ramps as high as 30 feet, perhaps by as few as ten men. The islanders "were incredible engineers," says California State University archaeologist Carl Lipo, who's mapped more than a hundred pukao with the University of Hawaii's Terry Hunt. "They used the least amount of labor they needed to get something done—all without cranes." —*Hannah Bloch*

Pukao can be up to eight feet high. Final touches like a top knob may have been added after a hat was hoisted onto a head.

Not all *moai* were created equal; those with "hats" probably had higher status.

PHOTOS: PHIL MARION (ABOVE); PRESS ASSOCIATION/AP IMAGES. NGM MAPS

Camino
de Santiago

Left: Imposing baroque facade of the cathedral at Santiago de Compostela (Galicia)
Right: Statue of St. James in pilgrim attire, Santiago de Compostela (Galicia)
Below: The Way of St. James crosses the Cebreiro Pass (Galicia)

The Way of St. James

For more than a thousand years the ancient Way of St. James has drawn pilgrims and travelers across the breadth of Northern Spain. In medieval times, routes from every corner of Europe converged in the foothills of the Pyrenees before braving the high passes and challenging overland trek to Santiago de Compostela in Galicia, legendary resting place of St. James (Santiago). Initially pilgrims banded together for safety, most adopting an inland route across the plains, El Camino Francés (The French Way), while others struck out along the north coast.

As the cult of St. James grew, pilgrims, artists, merchants, knights, and knaves, created a cultural highway rich in magnificent art and architecture, pilgrim hospices, and prosperous cities. The pilgrim road still exerts a powerful influence today, attracting around 100,000 visitors a year. Midway through the 2010 Holy Year, almost 180,000 pilgrims had already collected their *compostelas* (certificates of pilgrimage). For some it is a religious or spiritual journey, others are inspired by curiosity and the desire to slow down and discover the diverse natural beauty and historic cities of northern Spain at a gentler pace. The Way of St. James offers a rare opportunity to follow the thread of a fascinating pilgrim history through the individual Regions of the Way, each stamped with its own distinctive personality and age-old traditions.

The French Way is the best documented pilgrim route to Santiago. Divided into 39 stages of 20-30 kilometers from the Pyrenean crossings at Orreaga/Roncesvalles and Somport, a single course emerges at Puente la Reina, and heads west through Rioja, and Castille y León to Galicia.

Pictures, left to right:
1. Cathedral of San Pedro, Jaca (Aragon)
2. Pilgrim monastery of San Juan de la Peña (Aragon)
3. Pilgrim church of San Pedro de la Rúa, Estella (Navarra)
4. Landscape in seasonal color (La Rioja)
5. Cathedral of Santa María de Regla, León (Castille y León)

The French Way

Jaca, Puente la Reina, Logroño, Santo Domingo de la Calzada, Burgos, León, Ponferrada, and Santiago de Compostela

Orreaga/Roncesvalles, high in the mountainous medieval kingdom of Navarra, was the traditional gateway to Spain. This unspoiled and ruggedly beautiful region is renowned for its hospitality and a host of

festivals and cultural activities associated with pilgrim tradition. The other historic route, via the Somport Pass (1,632 meters/5,355 feet) in neighboring Aragon, swoops down past heart-stopping views from the famous Bridge of Canfranc to Jaca. The historic capital of the Aragonese kingdom, Jaca's influential bishops founded Spain's first Romanesque cathedral, San Pedro. West of the city, the outstanding pilgrim monastery of San Juan de la Peña is partially hewn from the rocky mountainside. Carved scallop shells decorate the porch of the Knights Templars' church at Puente la Reina, where the Pyrenean routes converge to continue into Rioja, a name redolent of great Spanish wines.

Today vineyards and olive groves accompany the pilgrim road to the wine centre of Logroño. At Santo Domingo de la Calzada, one of the Way's most famous traditions is the white cockerel and chicken kept in the cathedral. They recall a miracle performed by St. Domingo, who revived a wrongly accused and executed pilgrim and the cooked chicken the judge who sentenced him was about to eat for lunch.

The joint provinces of Castille and León lie at the heart of the Way, which links two superb medieval cities offering an abundance of world-class sites and museums augmented

by a wide-ranging cultural agenda. Burgos' great cathedral is a masterpiece of Spanish Gothic architecture housing the tomb of El Cid, revered warrior-general of the Reconquest. On the outskirts of the city, exceptional 12th-century Mudejar decoration in the Monasterio de Las Huelgas bears the imprint of Moorish culture alongside the elaborate tombs of Castilian monarchs. Burgos' newest attraction is the Museum of Human Evolution.

The superb High Gothic cathedral at León is celebrated for its stained glass, while a short step away, the Collegiate Church of San Isidoro is a Romanesque gem, its royal Pantheon decorated with exceptional 12th-century wall paintings.

Beyond the imposing Templar castle at Ponferrada, the Way begins the final arduous trek into the mountains entering Galicia near the misty heights of O Cebreiro, site of a pre-Romanesque pilgrim chapel and primitive, circular *palloza* stone dwellings.

Galicia is the final link in the pilgrim way, where the golden stone city of Santiago de Compostela rises from the green folds of the Gallego landscape like an apparition. All roads lead to the sprawling cathedral and monumental buildings of the vast Plaza del Obradoiro. The atmospheric midday pilgrim Mass in the cathedral is an unmissable occasion and a chance to admire the superb carved Pórtico de la Gloria. Climb up to the roof, too, for stupendous views and savour the city's unique atmosphere as the latest arrivals reach their destination footsore but elated.

The Northern Route

Hondarribia, Bilbao, Santander, Santillana del Mar, Llanes, Oviedo, Mondoñedo, Lugo, and finally Santiago de Compostela

XACOBEO 2010

ERDF
European Regional Development Fund
EUROPEAN UNION
"A way of building Europe"

The Legend

The coastal pilgrim way was never as well defined as the Camino Francés, but it too can be followed in stages on a cliff-hugging roller-coaster ride from Basque country through the verdant Green Spain of Cantabria and Asturias to Galicia.

Just over the French border, Hondarribia is a picture book Basque village of half-timbered houses clinging to perpendicular cobbled streets, balconies overflowing with geraniums, and a four-square fort above the harbor. The broad, sandy bay of Playa de la Concha fronts the handsome seaside town of Donostia-San Sebastian. This is a good place to sample traditional Basque cuisine and local Txakoli wines. Following

the coastline, Markina-Xemein's walled old quarter retains a distinctive medieval charm, before the tranquil valleys of the Lea-Artibai region lead to Bilbao, and the breathtaking Guggenheim Museum of contemporary art.

Cantabria's lush, rural hinterland unfurls past a string of appealing former whaling ports turned seaside resorts. At Castro-Urdiales, the fortress-like 13th-century church of Santa María de la Asunción broods over the port, and seafront houses sport tall *solanas* (glassed-in wooden balconies). From elegant Santander, the next stage of the journey leads to Santillana del Mar, a beautifully preserved historic town of cobbled streets and Renaissance mansions packed tightly around a

12th-century Romanesque church. The intricately carved capitals in the cloister are among the finest in Spain. Just west of town, a museum by the famous Altamira caves re-creates the prehistoric rock paintings adorning the caverns. Outlined against the mountainous backdrop of the Cordillera Cantabrica, San Vicente de la Barquera lies on a broad estuary studded with brightly-colored fishing boats. Here, the historic Camino Lebaniego detours from the coast, skirting the 2,000-meter (8,000-foot) Picos de Europa, to the monastery of Santo Toribio de Liébana, a revered pilgrimage center dating back to the 7th century.

The jagged Cordillera marks the border with Asturias, the sole Spanish territory never conquered by the Moors. This unspoiled "Natural

Paradise" is home to wild boar, deer, native Asturcon horses, the occasional brown bear, and soaring vultures. As the coastal scenery grows increasingly wild, the Northern branch of the pilgrim route continues west along the coastline, past hidden beach coves, impressive *bufones* (blowholes) near Llanes, and tiny, briny fishing ports clinging like barnacles to deep fissures in the cliffs known as *rías*. From Ribadeo, the final inland leg to Santiago leads through Mondoñedo, a handsome riverside town gathered around its Romanesque cathedral containing frescoes, a relic of the True Cross, and a fine museum.

An alternative to the final stages of the Northern Route, the Original Way from Oviedo

was the first recorded pilgrim route to Santiago, traveled by King Alfonso II of Asturias in the 9th century. Oviedo's compact old town, pressed around a fine Gothic cathedral, is a friendly place, well supplied with *siderias* serving local cider. In the beech woods just north of the city, the exquisite 9th-century church of Santa María del Naranco, originally a royal hunting lodge, is a UNESCO World Heritage site. Before reaching journey's end at Santiago, the ancient Roman settlement of Lugo is a popular stop. This delightful cathedral town boasts a 2-kilometer-long (1.5-mile) walk around spectacular Roman walls and the nearby temple of Santa Eulalia de Boveda, decorated with rare paleo-Christian frescoes.

Santiago's pilgrim tradition originated as the Moorish armies of Al-Mansur advanced through the very heart of Spain in the 9th century. According to legend, a marble sarcophagus containing the remains of the apostle martyred by Herod in 44 A.D. was rediscovered circa 810, several centuries after it had washed ashore on the wild Galician coast following a miraculous voyage from Judea. This astonishing tale, swiftly endorsed by the church, seized the imagination of Europeans living in fear of Moorish invasion. St. James became a rallying call to the Christian faithful, appearing as heroic Santiago Matamoros (the Moorslayer) on the battlefield, and opening the byways of northern Spain to seven centuries of pilgrim traffic. The third holiest Christian site, after Jerusalem and Rome, Santiago attracted as many as a half million visitors a year at the height of its importance in the 11th-12th centuries. Notable pilgrims included the Emperor Charlemagne, Louis VII of France, St. Francis of Assisi, and Chaucer's Wife of Bath. In 1589, Sir Francis Drake and the English Fleet landed at La Coruña, and the relics were hidden for safety. Lost for 300 years, they resurfaced in 1879, when pilgrimages resumed.

Pictures, left to right:
1. Traditional Basque houses, Hondarribia (Basque Country)
2. Guggenheim Museum, Bilbao (Basque Country)
3. Monastery of Santo Toribio de Liébana (Cantabria)
4. Renaissance mansions, Santillana del Mar (Cantabria)
5. Old Town, Oviedo (Asturias)
6. Cordillera Cantabrica (Asturias)
7. Fishing harbor, Luarca (Asturias) Infoasturias M.A.S.
8. Night time in Santiago de Compostela (Galicia)

For more information please go to
www.spain.info
www.turismodearagon.com   www.euskaditurismo.net
www.turismo.navarra.es   www.cantabriainfinita.es
www.lariojaturismo.com   www.infoasturias.com
www.turismocastillayleon.com   www.xacobeo.es

The Northern and Primitive Route
The French Way

0 ———— 40 mi
0 ———— 40 km

WILD

White markings distinguish *Giraffa camelopardalis peralta* from Africa's eight other subspecies.

A Tall Order Fourteen years ago the giraffes of West Africa were a neck away from extinction. A century of war, poaching, and habitat loss had nearly eradicated their range and their ranks, leaving fewer than 50. Yet today, says Julian Fennessy of the Giraffe Conservation Foundation, more than 220 are living alongside 80,000 farmers and villagers in a 150-mile-long zone near Niamey, Niger.

What accounts for this unlikely rebound? Expert Pierre Gay says conservation groups have extended micro-loans and agricultural aid to locals as an incentive to leave the animals be. The area also has ample food—acacia and *Combretum* leaves—and no predators, since hunters long ago wiped out the region's lions and leopards. Finally, Niger banned giraffe hunting in 1998, when it realized it had a unique, 18-foot-tall tourist lure: West Africa's only remaining herds.

Still, Fennessy warns that illegal wood cutting persists, that the population must reach 400 to be insulated from disease, and that individuals that have strayed from Niger's "giraffe zone" into neighboring countries have been killed. The next step is to increase the zone—and with it hope for a complete comeback. —*Jeremy Berlin*

Giraffe herds once roamed West Africa from Niger to the Atlantic. Today they exist only in Niger.

Learn more about wildlife on the Nat Geo WILD TV network. Visit **natgeowild.com**.

Designers are creating innovative, affordable products as solutions to problems all over the world.

Big Ideas

Little Packages

CAN GOOD DESIGN SAVE THE WORLD? It just might, one novel idea at a time. Designers have always dreamed up innovative goods for those who could afford such things: New offerings include solar roof tiles, electric motorcycles, and more. Now, sparked by programs such as the Entrepreneurial Design for Extreme Affordability course at Stanford University's Institute of Design (source for several items on these pages), some are taking a look at the concerns of people in developing countries as well. Keeping local culture in mind, designers are creating products to meet communities' particular needs. It turns out that even the most pressing problems, from health care to potable water, can have affordable—and beautifully designed—solutions. —*Margaret G. Zackowitz*

Infant Warmer

Around 19 million low-birth-weight babies are born every year in developing countries. Unable to regulate their body temperatures, many die. The Embrace helps to warm vulnerable infants (a special pouch slips into the back of the bag to provide hours of safe heat) while allowing for nursing and cuddling.

Developed by Jane Chen, Linus Liang, Naganand Murty, Rahul Panicker
Website *embraceglobal.org*
Launch country India

Asthma Device

Young asthmatics often can't coordinate breathing with the aerosol puff dispensed by inhalers. The folded-paper Respira "spacer" traps medication around the mouth so that it can be inhaled. Conventional spacers can run $20 or more—a prohibitive cost in the developing world, where asthma rates are rising. Respira costs about a dollar.

Developed by Eric Green, Santiago Ocejo, Barry Wohl
Website *respiradesign.org*
Launch country Mexico

Purifying Straw

Some 900 million people lack access to safe drinking water. Sipping through the LifeStraw filters surface water on-site, reducing the transmission of bacteria and viruses. Thousands of ten-inch LifeStraws were donated to Haiti after this year's earthquake. Each filters about 160 gallons; a new, shorter model, nearly 265.

Developed by
Vestergaard Frandsen
Website *lifestraw.com*
Launch country Kenya

Water Container

In impoverished rural areas, clean water is often miles away from the people who need it, leaving them susceptible to waterborne diseases. The sturdy Q Drum holds 13 gallons in a rolling container that eases the burden of transporting safe, potable water—a task that falls mostly to women and children.

Developed by
P. J. and J. P. S. Hendrikse
Website *qdrum.co.za*
Launch country South Africa

SOME OF THE OBJECTS ON THESE PAGES ARE COURTESY OF THE EXHIBIT "DESIGN FOR THE OTHER 90%" BY THE SMITHSONIAN COOPER-HEWITT, NATIONAL DESIGN MUSEUM.
PHOTOS: REBECCA HALE, NGM STAFF (WARMER); MARK THIESSEN, NGM STAFF (INHALER); RENEE COMET (LIFESTRAW, Q DRUM)

Chili Grinder

Ethiopian women have for centuries crushed chili peppers by hand—a time-consuming, painful way to add value to a staple spice. The Pepper Eater mills chilies four times faster, creating uniform flakes and sparing hands from chili-oil burns.

Developed by Samuel Hamner, Scott Sadlon
Website *thepeppereater.org*
Launch country Ethiopia

Sugarcane Charcoal

Burning wood and dung, the main fuel sources for many in the developing world, has contributed to deforestation and respiratory ailments. Not only do briquettes made from crushed sugarcane stalks make use of an abundant local resource, they burn more cleanly and allow residents to start a charcoal business for less than $50.

Developed by MIT D-Lab
Website *d-lab.mit.edu/resources*
Launch country Haiti

Portable Clay Cooler

Building upon an ancient food-storage technique, the pot-in-pot system uses evaporation from a layer of wet sand between two nesting pots to help extend the life of farmers' goods. Tomatoes can last weeks instead of just days, meaning more fresh produce at the market and more income for farmers.

Developed by Mohammed Bah Abba
Website none available
Launch country Nigeria

SONY
make.believe

α

Life moves pretty fast

Catch it at 10 frames per second.

The new α55 from Sony
offers you high speed
continuous shooting at up to
10 frames per second,
or 7 fps with the α33.

Both cameras are
equipped with unique
Translucent Mirror
Technology which
delivers precise, ultra-fast
autofocus, whether you're
shooting still pictures of
fast moving subjects or
Full HD movies.

sony.co.uk/highspeed

Image: Nick Webster

Full HD 1080   Translucent Mirror Technology   3D   3D Sweep Panorama   α55   α33

SONY   α

α55

Solar Roof Tiles

Solé Power Tiles may look like blue versions of the clay roof tiles traditionally used in sunny climes, but they're made of a durable polymer—and they're actually curved photovoltaic solar panels, creating enough energy daily to cut a typical American home's electric bill by 70 percent or more.

Developed by SRS Energy
Website *srsenergy.com*
Launch country U.S.

Solar Light

Hazardous kerosene lamps are the only source of lighting for millions of people all over the world. The solar-powered MightyLight is safer, cleaner, and more versatile: It can be hung on a wall, placed on a tabletop, or carried. It also lasts longer—its LED technology is good for up to 30 years of use.

Developed by
Amit Chugh, Matthew Scott
Website *cosmosignite.com*
Launch country India

Electric Motorcycle

Made mostly from recycled materials, the Enertia "refuels" at either 110-volt or 220-volt electrical sockets. It travels at up to 60 miles an hour, emits no exhaust, and goes more than 40 miles between charges. The faster Empulse, with longer battery life, is due out in 2011.

Developed by
Brian Wismann
Website *brammo.com*
Launch country U.S.

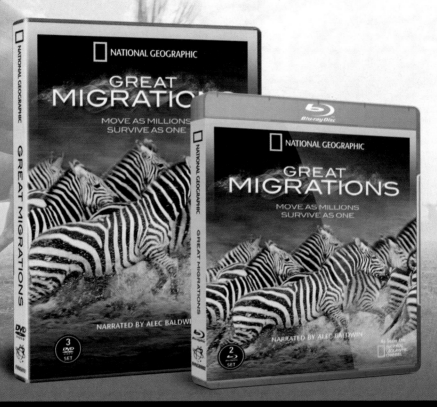

'Tis the season for giving NATIONAL GEOGRAPHIC!

ONE-YEAR NATIONAL GEOGRAPHIC SOCIETY MEMBERSHIP
€38.00

ORDER NOW and get a FREE Fleece Jacket!*

1. Complete this form and return it in the attached envelope.

Send 12 monthly issues of NATIONAL GEOGRAPHIC magazine... ☐ as a gift.   ☐ to me.

MY NAME

Please print. (Mr., Mrs., Miss, Ms.)

_____

Street Address

_____

City, Region

_____

Country, Postal Code

_____

E-mail (to receive e-mail updates and special offers from NGS)

GIFT FOR

Please print. (Mr., Mrs., Miss, Ms.)

_____

Street Address

_____

City, Region

_____

Country, Postal Code

2. Payment method *(Please tick one.)*:

☐ Cheque enclosed for €_____, payable to National Geographic Society.

Charge my ☐ Visa   ☐ MasterCard
           ☐ American Express.

Acct. no.:_____

Exp. date:_____

Signature:_____

Total fees: €_____   NFCKQZ8

Membership will begin with the January 2011 issue. Please allow 8–12 weeks for delivery of the first issue and your FREE gift. While all fees support the Society's mission of expanding geographic knowledge, 90 percent is designated for the magazine subscription.

A gift announcement card will be sent to you to present or post to your recipient.

We occasionally make our customer lists available to carefully screened companies whose products or services we feel may be of interest to you. If you prefer not to receive such mailings, please tick box. ☐

*Your FREE National Geographic Fleece Jacket will be sent to you upon order payment so that you may keep it or present it to your recipient.

▶ *Detach here and return in attached envelope. Thank you for your order!*

Solar Wi-Fi Streetlight

The StarSight system provides a series of pylons that use solar panels to power streetlamps, a Wi-Fi box for wireless Internet access, and if desired, closed-circuit TVs for security surveillance. The result: an integrated system of electricity and communication, plus better street lighting, which has been shown to help reduce crime.

Developed by
Kolam Partnership Ltd.
Website
starsightproject.com
Launch countries
Nigeria, South Africa, Turkey

Hearing-aid Recharger

The high cost of imported batteries can render hearing aids unaffordable for people in developing nations. This solar recharger accepts specially fitted hearing aids and standard rechargeable batteries, making hearing help less costly. More than 6,000 units are already in use in Africa, South and Central America, and Asia.

Developed by
Godisa Technologies Trust
Website none available
Launch country Botswana

Affordable Laptops

The One Laptop per Child project aims to educate children in remote parts of the world. Governments purchase the computers, each equipped with Wi-Fi "rabbit ears" and e-book mode, for schools. Uruguay has already distributed some 400,000 laptops, with another 90,000 on order. A tablet version is due in 2012.

Developed by Nicholas Negroponte, Rodrigo Arboleda Halaby
Website *laptop.org*
Launch country Brazil

Half a million sandhill cranes pause on the Platte River in Nebraska to fatten up on corn waste, worms, and other food in nearby fields. The break occurs on their spring flight from Mexico and the southern U.S. to breeding grounds in the far north.

Great Migrations

WHAT IS IT THAT MAKES ANIMAL
MIGRATION SUCH A MAGNIFICENT
SPECTACLE FOR THE EYE AND THE MIND?
Is it the sheer abundance of wildlife in
motion? Is it the steep odds to be overcome?
Is it the amazing feats of precise navigation?
The answer is all of the above. But there's another reason why the long-distance journeys of wildebeests,
sandhill cranes, monarch butterflies,
sea turtles, and so many other species inspire our
awe. One biologist has noted the "undistractibility" of
migrating animals. A nonscientist,
risking anthropomorphism, might say: Yes,
they have a sense of larger purpose.

Tens of millions of bison once rumbled across the Great Plains on a quest for grazing. By the late 1800s nearly all had been slaughtered. Today most of the half million remaining bison are in captivity, like these on the Triple U ranch in South Dakota.

Millions of monarch butterflies travel to ancestral winter roosts in Mexico's shrinking mountain fir forests. Surfing winds from southern Canada and the northern U.S., they travel thousands of miles, taking directional cues from the sun.

By David Quammen

Photographs by Joel Sartore

Animal migration is a phenomenon far grander and more patterned than animal movement. It represents collective travel with long-deferred rewards. It suggests premeditation and epic willfulness, codified as inherited instinct. A biologist named Hugh Dingle, striving to understand the essence, has identified five characteristics that apply, in varying

degrees and combinations, to all migrations. They are prolonged movements that carry animals outside familiar habitats; they tend to be linear, not zigzaggy; they involve special behaviors of preparation (such as overfeeding) and arrival; they demand special allocations of energy. And one more: Migrating animals maintain a fervid attentiveness to the greater mission, which keeps them undistracted by temptations and undeterred by challenges that would turn other animals aside.

An arctic tern on its way from Tierra del Fuego to Alaska, for instance, will ignore a nice smelly herring offered from a bird-watcher's boat in Monterey Bay. Local gulls will dive voraciously for such handouts, while the tern flies on. Why? "Animal migrants do not respond to sensory inputs from resources that would readily elicit responses in other circumstances," is the dry, careful way Dingle describes it. In plainer words: These critters are hell-for-leather, flat-out just *gonna get there.* Another way, less scientific, would be to say that the arctic tern resists distraction because it is driven at that moment by an instinctive sense of something we humans find admirable: larger purpose.

The arctic tern senses that it can eat later. It can rest later. It can mate later. Right now its implacable focus is the journey; its undivided intent is arrival. Reaching some gravelly coastline in the Arctic, upon which other arctic terns have converged, will serve its larger purpose, as shaped by evolution: finding a place, a time, and a set of circumstances in which it can successfully hatch and rear offspring.

But the process is complex as well as various,

Mountain goats in Montana's Glacier National Park may travel thousands of feet a day—vertically. This one descended a sheer rock wall to lick salt and other exposed minerals. Nutrients that aren't as available during the long winter may trigger the hankering.

and different biologists define it differently, depending in part on what sorts of animals they study. Joel Berger, of the Wildlife Conservation Society and the University of Montana, who works on the American pronghorn and other large terrestrial mammals, prefers what he calls a simple, practical definition suited to his beasts: "Movements from a seasonal home area away to another home area and back again." Generally the reason for such seasonal back-and-forth movement is to seek resources that aren't available within a single area year-round. But daily vertical movements by zooplankton in the ocean—upward by night to seek food, downward by day to escape predators—can also be considered migration. So can the movement of aphids when, having depleted the young leaves on one food plant, their offspring then fly onward to a different host plant, with no one aphid ever returning to where it started.

Dingle, an evolutionary biologist who studies insects, offers a more intricate definition than Berger's, citing those five features (persistence, linearity, undistractibility, special start-and-stop behaviors, stored energy) that distinguish migration from other forms of movement. For example, aphids will become sensitive to blue light (from the sky) when it's time for takeoff on their big journey and sensitive to yellow light (reflected from tender young leaves) when it's appropriate to land. Birds will fatten themselves with heavy feeding in advance of a long migrational flight. The value of his definition, Dingle argues, is that it focuses attention on what the phenomena of the wildebeests and the sandhill cranes share with the phenomenon of the aphids and therefore helps guide researchers toward understanding how evolution by natural selection has produced them all.

RATTLESNAKE MIGRATION on the Great Plains of western Canada is a peculiar but illuminating case. A young Canadian biologist named Dennis Jørgensen, now employed by the World Wildlife Fund, studied movements of the prairie rattlesnake (*Crotalus viridis viridis*) on the outskirts of Medicine Hat, Alberta, near the northern limit of its range, and found the snakes migrating ambitiously each spring and fall. The average round-trip by his animals was about 5 miles, though an earlier study detected Canadian rattlesnakes migrating as far as 33 miles. In Arizona, by contrast, rattlers don't travel nearly so far, because they don't have to. The driving logic of the Canadian migrations is related to cold winter temperatures (always difficult for reptiles) and the scarcity of really good den sites in which to survive hibernation.

"There aren't many dens that can support survival over winter on this landscape," Jørgensen told me. An ideal den must be deep underground, where the earth is warm, but accessible from the surface via burrows or natural fissures. Such refuges are few and far between. "Because of that, what you get is very large aggregations of snakes at these communal dens." Picture a serpentine tangle of a thousand snakes, piled together cozily, calm and sleek in their subterranean nook, jointly awaiting the signals of spring. When surface temperatures rise to a comfortable threshold, they emerge. For a while they bask in the sunlight, crowded like bronzed tourists on the Costa del Sol. But the rattlesnakes are hungry. What's their next imperative? To get away from one another, find food, and mate. So they migrate radially—in all possible directions away from the den—like starburst embers from a Fourth of July rocket.

Jørgensen used small radio transmitters, surgically implanted, to chart this pattern, tracking the individual routes of 28 different rattlesnakes during 2004 and 2005. More recently, on a blazing summer day, he took me back to one of the den sites, in a slumping bank above the South Saskatchewan River. The slumping had opened deep underground cracks in which roughly 60 prairie rattlers had wintered. From the riverbank we turned toward the uplands and began retracing the migration route of one of his animals, an ambitious female he had labeled E.

Not far upslope were three rounded boulders, lichen-covered, with a hole beneath. Snake E had arrived here on May 8, Jørgensen said; she rested, basked, and took off again on May 27. She ascended this steep bench (we started climbing) amid the sage and crumbling gray mud, then slithered back down the slope (we plunged after her), crossed this dirt road, crossed this moist gulch full of goldenrod and skunkbrush

Contributing Writer David Quammen is the author of 11 books, including The Reluctant Mr. Darwin. *Nebraska-based Joel Sartore specializes in covering biodiversity. This is his 30th story for the magazine.*

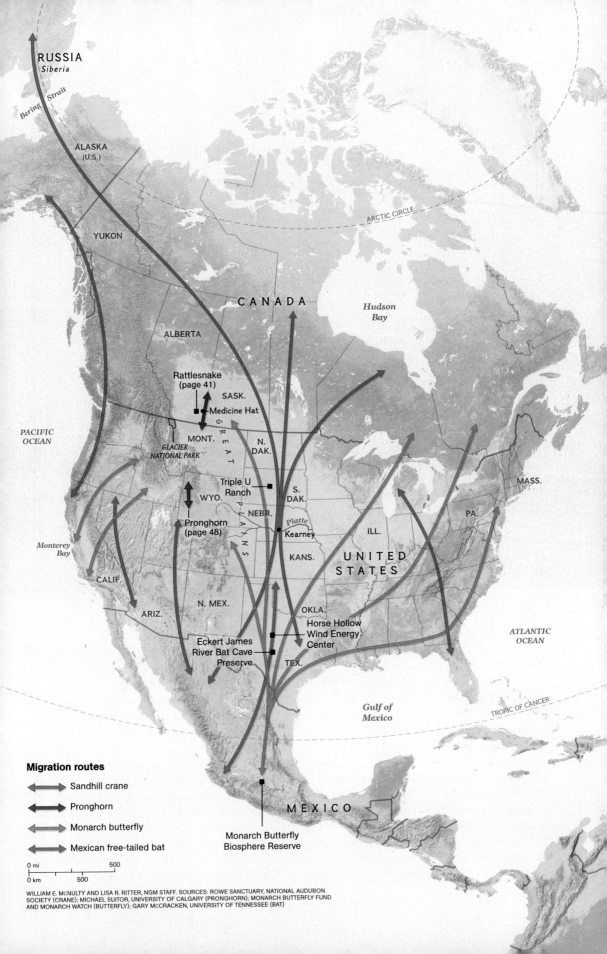

RUSSIA
Siberia

Bering Strait

ALASKA
(U.S.)

YUKON

ARCTIC CIRCLE

PACIFIC OCEAN

ALBERTA

CANADA

Hudson Bay

Rattlesnake
(page 41)

SASK.

Medicine Hat

GLACIER NATIONAL PARK

MONT.

G R E A T

N. DAK.

MASS.

Triple U
Ranch

S. DAK.

WYO.

NEBR.

P L A I N S

Platte

Kearney

ILL.

PA.

Monterey Bay

Pronghorn
(page 48)

KANS.

U N I T E D
S T A T E S

CALIF.

N. MEX.

ARIZ.

OKLA.

Horse Hollow
Wind Energy
Center

ATLANTIC OCEAN

Eckert James
River Bat Cave
Preserve

TEX.

Gulf of Mexico

TROPIC OF CANCER

Migration routes

Sandhill crane

Pronghorn

Monarch butterfly

Mexican free-tailed bat

M E X I C O

Monarch Butterfly
Biosphere Reserve

0 mi   500
0 km   500

WILLIAM E. McNULTY AND LISA R. RITTER, NGM STAFF. SOURCES: ROWE SANCTUARY, NATIONAL AUDUBON SOCIETY (CRANE); MICHAEL SUITOR, UNIVERSITY OF CALGARY (PRONGHORN); MONARCH BUTTERFLY FUND AND MONARCH WATCH (BUTTERFLY); GARY McCRACKEN, UNIVERSITY OF TENNESSEE (BAT)

(we thrashed through), and climbed again. Back atop the bench, we ducked between strands of barbed wire into the corner of a crop field irrigated by center pivot. The crop had been alfalfa when E came through; this year, potatoes. We politely circumvented the spud field and picked up her track on the far side, between several more center-pivot circles, blooming bright yellow and rank with canola. The midday air, hot and thick, smelled like baked fish from an oven.

Having sprinted across two pivot fields in a single day, brave lady, E had then picked up the security of a fence line, where the weeds were dense and the discs of a tiller, the blades of a swather, never touched. By late June she was making

200 yards daily, still along the fence line, amid a hospitable jumble of rocks, weeds, and rodent burrows. At that point Jørgensen and I paused in the shade of a cottonwood to rest. We had covered eight weeks of rattlesnake migration in four hours and were drenched with sweat.

Hereabouts was where E had spent most of her summer that year, mating at least once and fattening herself on rodents for the homeward migration, another winter in the den, and pregnancy. It was productive habitat but also risky, Jørgensen said, what with all the agricultural machinery that could dice a snake like zucchini, all the farm-road traffic that could flatten her like an alligator belt. The changes that had

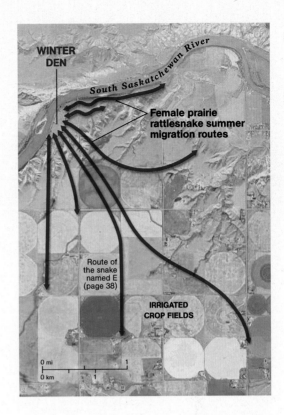

WINTER
DEN

South Saskatchewan River

Female prairie
rattlesnake summer
migration routes

Route of
the snake
named E
(page 38)

IRRIGATED
CROP FIELDS

0 mi   1
0 km   1

DEADLY CROSSINGS *Out of hibernation—and hungry—many species of snakes follow the same scent trails year after year, no matter the obstacles. A western cottonmouth (left) didn't survive the trip across a levee road in Illinois. Rattlesnakes on spring feeding forays from underground winter dens near Medicine Hat, Alberta (above), often meet a similar fate.*

come to this landscape did not favor long-distance rattlesnake migration. At that moment, as though to embody those changes within one human memory, a man named Aldo Pederzolli pulled up on his four-wheeler.

Pederzolli was the farmer on whose land we stood and who had genially welcomed Jørgensen's study. He wore a black polo shirt, rubber boots, and a cap that read "Cee-Gee Earthmoving." He was a fit-looking man of 80, with squinty brown eyes, a high voice, a sun-ripened Canadian smile. Introduced to me, hearing the reason for my visit, he said, "Oh, I just love rattlers." This wasn't irony. Got enough good snakes, he added, and you don't need to worry about

gophers. Back when he was young, Pederzolli recalled, he would see nice fat old rattlers, that big around, when he seeded a fallow field. Don't see such big ones anymore. There was a den near the river, he said wistfully, and they'd migrate six miles up to a nice patch of open prairie full of gophers. Not anymore.

Although it's only a hypothesis, Dennis Jørgensen suspects that natural selection—in this case, the death of the venturesome—may be turning his migrating rattlesnakes into a population of stay-at-homes.

BIOLOGICAL DIVERSITY entails more than a gross tally of species. Diversity of ecosystems,

MAP: NGM MAPS
SOURCE: DENNIS JØRGENSEN, WWF. SATELLITE IMAGE: GEOEYE

Mexican free-tailed bats spiral out of Eckert James River Bat Cave Preserve in Texas at dusk. The bats are hungry for pests like corn earworm moths— nutrition to keep milk flowing for their pups. Every spring millions of free-tails return to this cave

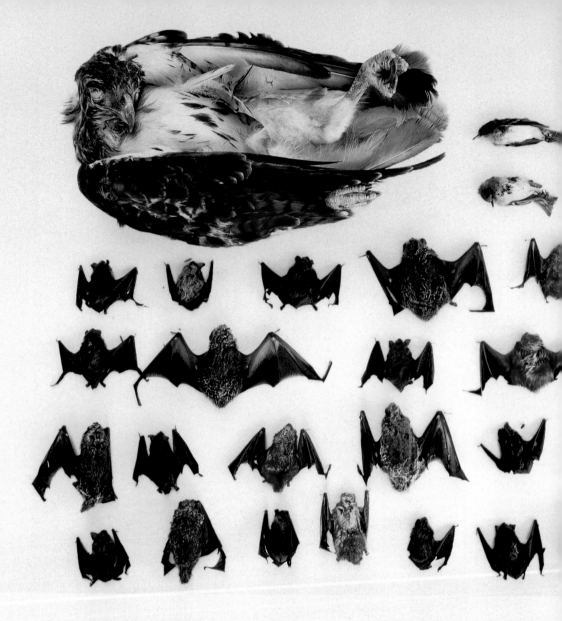

behaviors, and processes are important too, contributing richness and beauty, robustness and flexibility and interconnectedness to the living communities on Earth. To lose the long-distance migrations performed by some species would be a grievous diminution. Joel Berger has made this point in the journal *Conservation Biology* and elsewhere, with reference to migrating species around the world and one creature close to home: the pronghorn *(Antilocapra americana),* North America's only endemic species of ungulate.

Loose talk sometimes mistakes the pronghorn for an antelope, but in fact it belongs to a family all its own. Its extreme speed (fastest land mammal of the New World), more than necessary

to evade any living North American predator, probably reflects adaptation for escaping the now extinct American cheetah of the Pleistocene. Besides traveling fast, though, the pronghorn also travels far. One population migrates hundreds of miles across the Great Plains from north-central Montana into southern Saskatchewan and Alberta. Another population follows a narrow, tenuous route from its summer range in Grand Teton National Park, across a divide at the headwaters of the Gros Ventre River, and down onto the plains south of Pinedale, Wyoming, in the Green River Basin. There the pronghorn mingle with thousands of others arrived from other parts of Wyoming, where they try

FATAL TURBINES *These 32 bats and four song-birds represent an average yearly toll for each of the 23 turbines at a Pennsylvania wind farm. Raptors like the red-tailed hawk (left, top row) are rare victims. Horse Hollow wind farm near Abilene, Texas (above), one of the world's largest, has more than 400 turbines. A drop in air pressure from the spinning blades causes many of the bat deaths.*

to distance themselves from the natural gas wellheads and drilling teams, and wait out the frozen months, feeding mainly on sagebrush blown clear of snow.

The Grand Teton pronghorn are notable for the invariance of their migration path and the severity of its constriction at three critical spots, known as Trappers Point, the Red Hills, and the Funnel. Field research by Berger and colleagues has charted that path and illuminated its jeopardies. If the pronghorn can't pass through each of the three bottlenecks during their spring migration, they can't reach their bounty of summer grazing in Grand Teton National Park; if they can't pass through again in autumn, escaping south

onto those windblown plains, they'll likely die trying to overwinter in the Jackson Hole area or get fatally stuck in the deep snows of the divide. On a bright day in November, in company with a biologist named Renee Seidler, I went for a look at the details of their dilemma.

Seidler, also employed by the Wildlife Conservation Society, works mostly on habitat issues in the booming gas fields between Pinedale and Rock Springs, an area that supports perhaps 20,000 pronghorn each winter. The northward migrants constitute just a fraction of that total but are special, she noted, because without them, one of America's great western parks, Grand Teton, would entirely lack one of America's great

Pronghorn run fast—upwards of 60 miles an hour—but they rarely jump fences. Some ranchers plan to raise the lowest fence strands so pronghorn, like these near Medicine Hat, Alberta, can more easily slip under during their winter migration.

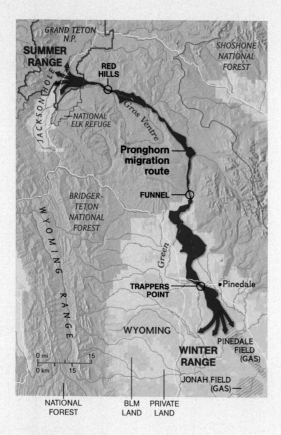

CONSTRICTED PASSAGE *Pronghorn migrating between summer and winter ranges in north-western Wyoming negotiate steep valleys, forested mountainsides, and a gantlet of man-made intrusions. New homes restrict the corridors to no more than a few hundred yards wide in places, and gas drilling projects, such as Jonah Field (right), also impede their migration.*

MAP: NGM MAPS. SOURCE: ANDRA TOIVOLA, WILDLIFE CONSERVATION SOCIETY

western species. On a knoll at Trappers Point, we read the historical marker about fur trappers and Nez Perce and Crow peoples gathering here to trade and gazed down at the modern manifestations of growth and commerce alongside Highway 191: a sprawling little community known as Cora Junction. There were about 50 houses, trailers, and other buildings, including a Jehovah's Witnesses meeting hall, all nested within a grid of streets and lanes, fenced yards, dogs, chickens, real estate signs, old tires, boats on trailers, a weathered trampoline, and a rusting green Chrysler from the 1940s. Right about here, Seidler said, pointing to a gap of sage between our knoll and the houses, is where

most of the pronghorn seem to cross through.

We drove north on a county road about 20 miles, along willowy bottomlands of the upper Green River, tracing the migration route. Pronghorn, dependent on distance vision and speed to keep safe from predators, do not like willowy bottomlands, Seidler explained. They don't like dense forest either, so they traverse these high, open shoulders between the river and the woods, where they can see and run. Then we came to a place where forested hills rose on both sides of the river to form a soft V, leaving a corridor of open ground only about 150 yards wide. "That's the Funnel," Seidler said. It was private land, dissected by the driveways, the buck-and-rail

fences, the arched gateways of people wealthy enough to have a second home, or a third, on the headwaters of the Green. On this day, in the off-season, there was no sign of anyone around.

One more yard fence, one more house, one or two large barking dogs, could make a bad difference. As at Trappers Point so here at the Funnel; incremental human activities are accumulating toward a crisis for Grand Teton's pronghorn— threatening to choke off their passageway.

Conservation scientists such as Berger, along with some biologists and land managers within the National Park Service and other agencies, are now working to preserve migrational behaviors, not just species and habitats. The Bridger-Teton National Forest has recognized the path of the Grand Teton pronghorn, much of which passes across national forest land, as the first federally protected migration corridor. But neither the Forest Service nor the Park Service can control what happens on private land at a bottleneck, nor on Bureau of Land Management parcels within the drilling fields south of Pinedale. And with certain other migrating species, the challenge is complicated further—by vastly greater distances traversed, more jurisdictions, more borders, more dangers along the way.

IMAGINE, FOR INSTANCE, that you're a lesser sandhill crane (*Grus canadensis canadensis*), setting off

A border wall along the lower Rio Grande in Texas divides nations as well as habitats, hindering essential daily movements of animals in the area. Bobcats would normally cross the border to find mates or catch dinner—this one caught a rat. The wall also blocks the daily rounds of ocelots, another member of the cat family.

on your spring migration from southwestern Texas. You might have to fly across a corner of New Mexico and Oklahoma, then Kansas, Nebraska, South Dakota, North Dakota (most of which allow hunting of sandhills), then over the Canadian border into Saskatchewan, angling northwest across Alberta and British Columbia, across Yukon Territory, then the breadth of Alaska, and finally across the Bering Strait to your summer breeding grounds in northeastern Russia. This would be a trip of roughly 5,000 miles. Needing to pause somewhere and replenish yourself, you would probably stop on the Platte River in Nebraska, near the town of Kearney. If so, you'd have company. About 500,000 northbound sandhills make the same stopover every year.

There they linger for two or three weeks, maybe four. Some depart onward as others arrive, keeping the average crane count during March and April at around 300,000. By night they roost in the gently flowing shallows of the Platte, shin-deep in cool water, or else on sandbars, giving them warning against any predator that might come splashing out. Each morning they rise up in vast, graceful waves and fly to fields nearby, where they spend their days assiduously feeding on waste corn the harvesters missed and earthworms and other invertebrates. Such a stopover period is no exception to the undistractibility of migrating animals, as defined by Hugh Dingle; it's a part of the whole program, repeated by generations of cranes. During this stopover, a six-pound lesser sandhill adds about a pound and a half of fat to its weight. (The greater sandhill, another subspecies also present on the Platte, is larger.) The birds need that fat between Nebraska and Russia. Therefore, they need the stopover habitat—the shallows,

the sandbars, the security, the corn and invertebrates—to complete their arduous yearly cycle.

I stood overlooking that habitat, on a morning in late March, and watched wave after wave of cranes rise from the river. Each group climbed clumsily off the water, gained elegance as their wings caught more air, turned in formation, and flew out to their daily feeding. Meanwhile, they called to one another in their distinctive, creaky trill. There were maybe 60,000 sandhills just within the sweep of my binoculars. It was a spectacle of extraordinary abundance, a reminder of what America looked like back when John James Audubon stared up at sky-clogging flocks of passenger pigeons, when George

Catlin saw the thunderous migrations of bison.

I had watched fly-in of the cranes too, on an earlier evening, when they arrived back through the twilight and settled onto their shoals for the night. But I found fly-out more deeply affecting—because, I suppose, the birds at daybreak are headed off with a purpose, not just home to rest. They would fatten themselves for another long leg of their journey. Their travel would take them to safe and bountiful breeding grounds. Their prodigious efforts, their resistance to distraction, would yield new cohorts of sandhill cranes, extending and rejuvenating the species. I almost wrote "perpetuating the species," but no, we can't be sure of that. Nothing alive is perpetual.

It was the accrued wisdom and resoluteness of evolution that I was witnessing, airborne above the Platte. If we humans have accrued equal wisdom and can summon equal resoluteness, I thought, maybe we'll allow them to continue their journeying a while longer. ☐

GREAT MIGRATIONS

This seven-part global programming event follows the arduous journeys millions of animals undertake to ensure the survival of their species. Premiering in the U.S. on the **National Geographic Channel, Sunday, November 7 at 8 p.m. ET/PT.** Animal migrations come to life online with 3-D explorations of their epic travels at **natgeotv.com/migrations.**

GREAT MIGRATIONS

THE LOST HERDS OF SOUTHERN SUDAN

*Sudan's civil war ended in 2005.
Peace brought the welcome discovery
that the south still teems with
Africa's iconic animals.*

*Elephants kick up ash from a wildfire in the Sudd
wetland. The fires, often set by pastoralists,
underscore a new threat to wildlife: habitat loss.
Poaching remains an ever present danger.*

Thousands of white-eared kob race in the shadow of a Wildlife Conservation Society survey plane in a park east of Bor. The seasonal migration of animals in southern Sudan is a spectacle to rival the flow of animals across Tanzania's Serengeti Plain.

By Matthew Teague

Photographs by George Steinmetz

N ot long ago in Juba, in an old colonial building with cracked walls and fitful electricity, two former military men— Lt. Gen. Fraser Tong and Maj. Gen. Philip Chol Majak—were explaining the situation.

"Organized gangs, maybe 50 men, are coming in on horseback," Tong said. "They're targeting elephants and the bigger ungulates. They dry the meat and keep the ivory and transport it on camelback."

Tong is the undersecretary for wildlife in semi-autonomous southern Sudan, based in Juba, the capital. Majak is a senior staffer, a wildlife field commander whose army unit was famous for shooting down MiG jets with shoulder-fired missiles during Sudan's latest civil war, which began in 1983. A cease-fire ended that conflict five years ago, but now Majak is fighting a new war. "We have to protect these animals," he said.

There's urgency in his voice. He and his fellow southern Sudanese feel a deep kinship with their wildlife. It's deeper than people elsewhere might realize, because for generations foreign raiders harvested two goods from here: slaves and ivory. People and elephants became linked, almost synonymous, rounded up and shipped off together.

The bond strengthened during the civil war. As bombs and land mines exploded, humans who didn't flee into surrounding countries hid in the bush. So did elephants and other migratory beasts; some fell to hunters, but many evaded gunfire by finding refuge in hard-to-reach places.

Matthew Teague wrote about the Uygurs of China's Xinjiang region last December. George Steinmetz began his photographic career in Africa 30 years ago.

Wildlife experts struggle to place a GPS satellite collar on a tranquilized bull elephant in Boma National Park. A Wildlife Conservation Society project aims to track elephant migration to and from Ethiopia.

A floating fishing camp drifts in the Sudd, one of Africa's largest wetlands—more than 20,000 square miles in the rainy season. The scale of this place makes it difficult for wildlife authorities to patrol and enforce hunting and fishing laws.

As the dry season peaks and the waters in the Sudd recede, people at a Dinka fishing camp hunt anything they can find, like this Nile lechwe laid out on a hippo skin. They dry the meat on wooden racks. Authorities generally overlook subsistence hunting. Commercial poachers take advantage of the vast wilderness (map, right) to evade capture.

They became, in the minds of the southern Sudanese, fellow displaced victims of war. The more sedentary animals—buffalo, hartebeests, giraffes—were nearly wiped out. Soldiers hunted and ate the animals, but they also had rules: They would not shoot males, and they would try to avoid hunting any species to extinction.

The war dragged on. By the time it ended, no one knew how many animals remained or would return.

TWO YEARS LATER, three men—Paul Elkan, an American biologist who directs the Wildlife Conservation Society (WCS) program in southern Sudan, J. Michael Fay, also with WCS, and Malik Marjan, a southern Sudanese doctoral student at

the University of Massachusetts, Amherst—crisscrossed the landscape in a small plane, counting animals for the first time in decades. "It was stunning," Elkan told me. "Three-quarters of a million kob. Nearly 300,000 Mongalla gazelles. More than 150,000 tiang. Six thousand elephants." He came to a realization: "This is, hands down, one of the most important wild habitats in Africa."

WCS's aerial surveys have since been expanded to monitor wildlife, livestock, and human activity throughout much of southern Sudan. Elkan recently piloted his Cessna north of Juba, along the White Nile, then east into an immense territory that reached toward the sunrise. For hours we flew over untouched land. Rivers spontaneously surge here in the wet season, and wildfires rage

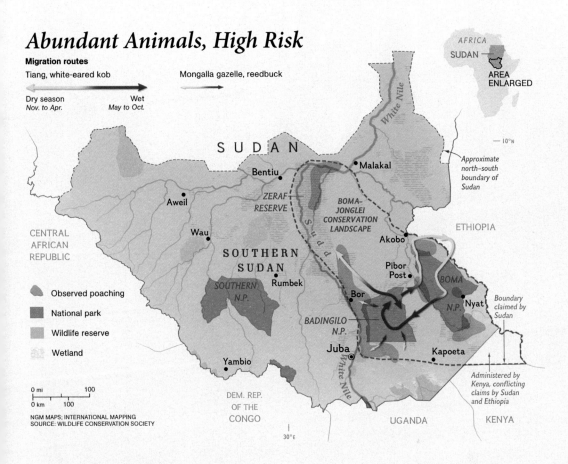

Abundant Animals, High Risk

Migration routes

Tiang, white-eared kob

Mongalla gazelle, reedbuck

Dry season
Nov. to Apr.

Wet
May to Oct.

AFRICA
SUDAN
AREA ENLARGED

— 10°N

Approximate north-south boundary of Sudan

SUDAN

Bentiu

Malakal

Aweil

ZERAF RESERVE

BOMA-JONGLEI CONSERVATION LANDSCAPE

ETHIOPIA

CENTRAL AFRICAN REPUBLIC

Wau

Akobo

SOUTHERN SUDAN

Pibor Post

BOMA

Observed poaching

SOUTHERN N.P.

Rumbek

Bor

N.P. Nyat

Boundary claimed by Sudan

National park

Wildlife reserve

BADINGILO N.P.

Wetland

Juba

Kapoeta

Yambio

0 mi   100
0 km   100

DEM. REP. OF THE CONGO

White Nile

Administered by Kenya, conflicting claims by Sudan and Ethiopia

NGM MAPS; INTERNATIONAL MAPPING
SOURCE: WILDLIFE CONSERVATION SOCIETY

30°E

UGANDA   KENYA

unchecked in the dry. "This is one of the largest intact savannas in Africa," he said.

He tipped down in the direction of a herd of white-eared kob, streaming north by the thousands. Some species have almost disappeared—there may be as few as seven zebras, devastated by hunting—but in the shadow of the plane, a lioness stalked gazelles. Elephant tracks, disks of mud, marched toward the horizon.

We landed on a dirt airstrip at Nyat, near the Ethiopian border, where village chiefs had gathered to hear about plans for wildlife conservation. Elkan delivered a revelation: The government of southern Sudan has banned hunting.

An elder raised his hand. "What about food?"

There's a big difference, Elkan replied, between a man who leaves his hut in the morning with a spear in his hand—as men have done here for thousands of years—and a hunter spraying

bullets from an automatic rifle. Or the commercial hunters coming down from the north to poach game. Rangers may overlook subsistence hunting outside the protected lands, which include the main wildlife migration corridors, Elkan said. But commercial hunting must stop.

WCS and the U.S. government are now working with southern Sudan's government to create a special area spanning some 77,000 square miles. It will encompass two national parks, a wildlife reserve, oil concessions, and community lands. If well managed and secure, Elkan explained, this huge region, so full of wildlife, will draw tourists, creating jobs and revenue. He urged them to spread the word.

The chiefs nodded. Southern Sudanese had fought a long, bloody war to win independence. Now the animals—their fellow survivors—deserved a peace of their own. ☐

SOUTHERN SUDAN
A SHAKY PEACE

Passage to manhood is literally incised on Majiek Gai Chan's face. Because Sudan's civil wars have claimed so many men, scarification is now performed on boys in the Nuer tribe as young as 12, instead of the traditional 15 to 18.

In September 2009 Nuer tribesmen attacked the Dinka village of Duk Padiet. The death toll of at least 167 included civilians as well as soldiers, adding to the lives lost in regional violence despite a 2005 treaty ending Sudan's most recent civil war. A UN helicopter evacuated the wounded.

Cattle—foundation of the Dinka economy—
speckle a floodplain in a camp near a branch of
the Nile during the dry season. The animals are
corralled at night to defend them against cattle
raiders, then taken out to graze during the day.

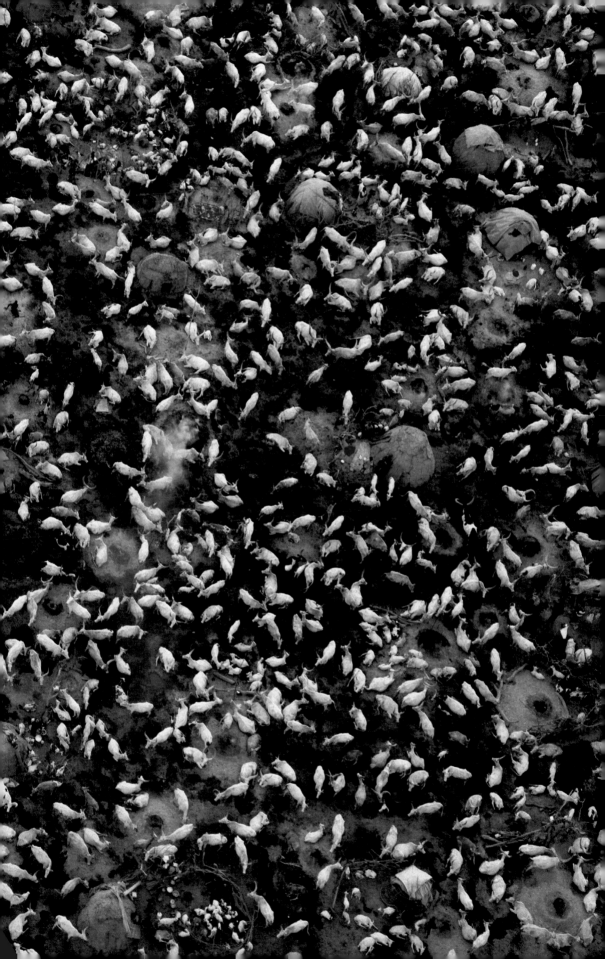

Villagers abandoned Nyiek during the civil war. Years later, after the peace treaty, they returned to find oil drillers had moved in—so they moved up the road, Little of the oil revenue trickles down: The village lacks both electricity and running water.

By Matthew Teague

Photographs by George Steinmetz

One day some years ago, before the latest civil war began in earnest, a Sudanese boy named Logocho peeked into the entry of his family's grass hut. His father sprang out and grabbed him, and then, with an older boy, pinned him in the dirt.

A strange boy, Logocho. Above him, his father's shoulders and chest rippled with welted tribal scars. A Morse code of dots and dashes crossed the father's face and forehead, signaling to any potential cattle raiders—the Dinka, the Nuer—that he, as a Murle, would defend his stock with spear, knife, fists, and teeth.

But his son showed no interest in the old ways. When other children, including his own brother, underwent an early Murle rite of passage, he ran and hid in the grass. Now his body, smooth as a calf's, trembled and arched in the dust. Nothing marked him as Murle.

More alarming, the nine-year-old boy showed no interest in cattle. Like his brother, Logocho crouched to suckle the udders of cows, but to him they meant only milk. For countless generations Murle men—and their rivals throughout southern Sudan—had lived alongside their cows. They named them, decorated them, slept beside them. Sang of them. Danced in their honor. Loved them. Men used cattle to purchase brides, who provided children, who tended more cows.

What is your purpose? Logocho's father asked.

While the men and beasts migrated from water to water, Logocho preferred to stay behind with his grandmother. The old woman scratched lines in the callous earth to grow sorghum and beans and maize and even pumpkins, and in lean seasons the men came to her with hands outstretched. Logocho helped her plant the seeds, tend the sprouts, and harvest the crops. She protected him from his father.

You are special, she would say.

She could not save him now, though. His father and the boy were holding him hard against the ground. *"Naa?"* Logocho cried. "Why?"

When he saw the "specialist," he knew. The man kneeled and bent over Logocho's face, then he reached for what looked like a thin metal file. He pried open the boy's jaw and wedged the blade between the two bottom middle teeth. He worked it down to the gum, and then with a wrench of his shoulder, he twisted it. Crack! An

The trademark hat worn by Salva Kiir, president of semiautonomous southern Sudan, was a gift from President George W. Bush during a summit. A former battlefield commander who has led the south since 2005, Kiir will guide his country through a referendum next year, when a vote for full independence is expected.

incisor splintered, and blood filled the moaning Logocho's mouth. The specialist reset the blade and—crack!—shattered the other middle tooth.

Now you look like a Murle.

In the next few months, chaos would descend on both Logocho and his homeland. A magician in the village would pronounce his family doomed. Across southern Sudan, the fury of generations would erupt in 1983 in a war both horrific and invisible to the outside world. During the next two decades more than four million southerners would flee their villages into the hinterlands, northern cities, and neighboring countries. Two million would die.

Logocho's life—fleeing, warring, searching for purpose—would share a trajectory with southern Sudan itself. But on this day, the boy's father released him and walked away with the

The specialist wedged the blade between Logocho's two bottom middle teeth. With a wrench of his shoulder, he twisted it. Crack! The incisors splintered. Now you look like a Murle.

specialist. Logocho rolled onto his side so the blood could pour from his mouth into the dust.

THE ORIGIN OF TENSIONS in Sudan is so geographic, so stark, you could see it even from the surface of the moon. The broad ivory of the Sahara in Africa's north set against the green savanna and jungles of the continent's narrowing center. A great, grass-stained tusk. Populations generally fall to one side or the other of that vegetative divide. Which side, north or south, largely defines the culture—religion, music, dress, language— of the people there. Sudan straddles that line to include arid desert in its north and grasslands and tropical rain forests in its south, and the estranged cultures on either side.

In Sudan, Arabs and black Africans had met with a clash. Islamic conquerors in the seventh century discovered that many inhabitants of the land then called Nubia were already Christian. The Nubians fought them to a stalemate that lasted more than a millennium, until the Ottoman governor based in Cairo invaded, exploiting the land south of Egypt as a reservoir of ivory and humans. In 1820 he enslaved 30,000 people known as Sudan, which meant simply "blacks."

Eventually global distaste for slavery put the slave traders out of business. The Ottomans retreated in the early 1880s, and in 1899, after a brief period of independence for Sudan, the British took control, ruling its two halves as distinct regions. They couldn't garrison all of Sudan—it's a massive country, ten times as big as the United Kingdom—so they ruled from Khartoum and gave limited powers to tribal leaders in the provinces. Meanwhile, they encouraged Islam and Arabic in the north and Christianity and English in the south. Putting effort and resources into the north, they left the south to languish. The question all this raises is:

Why? Why was a single Sudan created at all?

One reason, again, is geographic. As the Nile flows north toward Egypt, it binds the disparate cultures along its banks in a fitful, sometimes hateful, relationship. It defines trade, environment, even politics, linking the affairs of north and south. When the British ruled, they needed to control the Suez Canal at the Nile's mouth, because it linked Britain to the "jewel in the crown," India. That meant controlling the Nile, so no enemy could divert it.

When the British withdrew in the mid-1950s, there's little wonder the place fell into civil war. Southern rebels battled the northern government fiercely during the 1960s, and half a million people died before the two sides struck an agreement in 1972. Yet the pact only gave each side a chance to breathe deeply and rearm for what would be a much bloodier war.

During the lull between the two civil wars, the government in Khartoum joined Egypt to embark on a breathtaking project in the south. Where the Nile spreads across southern Sudan— that great tableland—it forms the Sudd, one of Africa's largest wetlands. And the river's annual floods rejuvenate grazing lands where southern tribes have long kept their cattle. The partners decided to build a 225-mile canal to shunt the river past the Sudd, due north to supply water-hungry Egypt. They brought in an eight-story digging machine, and tribesmen stood and watched as their pastures were ripped up.

At the start of the 1983 civil war, a rebel group called the Sudan People's Liberation Army (SPLA) formed, and in one of its first conspicuous acts, it attacked the Jonglei Canal construction headquarters, halting the project.

Years of bloodshed followed, ending in 2005 after extraordinary, behind-the-scenes diplomatic maneuvers brought about the Comprehensive Peace Agreement. This pact gave southern Sudan a measure of autonomy: its own constitution (based on separation of religion and state), army, and currency. Now Sudan finds itself wobbling between the possibility of lasting peace and the threat of fresh violence. In 2011, according to the pact, the people of southern Sudan will vote

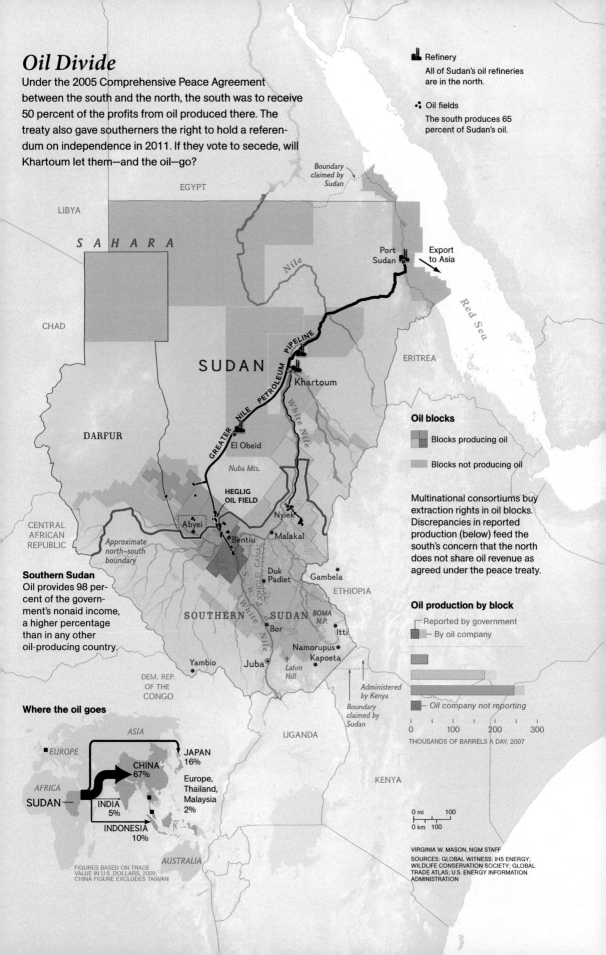

Oil Divide

Under the 2005 Comprehensive Peace Agreement between the south and the north, the south was to receive 50 percent of the profits from oil produced there. The treaty also gave southerners the right to hold a referendum on independence in 2011. If they vote to secede, will Khartoum let them—and the oil—go?

Refinery
All of Sudan's oil refineries are in the north.

Oil fields
The south produces 65 percent of Sudan's oil.

EGYPT

LIBYA

S A H A R A

Boundary claimed by Sudan

Nile

CHAD

Port Sudan

Export to Asia

Red Sea

ERITREA

S U D A N

PIPELINE

Khartoum

DARFUR

GREATER NILE PETROLEUM

El Obeid

Nuba Mts.

White Nile

Oil blocks

Blocks producing oil

Blocks not producing oil

HEGLIG OIL FIELD

Nyiek

CENTRAL AFRICAN REPUBLIC

Abyei

Approximate north-south boundary

Bentiu

Malakal

Multinational consortiums buy extraction rights in oil blocks. Discrepancies in reported production (below) feed the south's concern that the north does not share oil revenue as agreed under the peace treaty.

Southern Sudan
Oil provides 98 percent of the government's nonaid income, a higher percentage than in any other oil-producing country.

Duk Padiet

Gambela

ETHIOPIA

SOUTHERN SUDAN

BOMA N.P.

JONGLEI CANAL

White Nile

Bor

Itti

Oil production by block

Reported by government

By oil company

Namorupus

Kapoeta

Oil company not reporting

Yambio

Juba

Lafon Hill

0   100   200   300

THOUSANDS OF BARRELS A DAY, 2007

DEM. REP. OF THE CONGO

Administered by Kenya

Boundary claimed by Sudan

Where the oil goes

UGANDA

KENYA

ASIA

EUROPE

JAPAN 16%

CHINA 67%

Europe, Thailand, Malaysia 2%

AFRICA

SUDAN

INDIA 5%

INDONESIA 10%

AUSTRALIA

0 mi   100

0 km   100

VIRGINIA W. MASON, NGM STAFF
SOURCES: GLOBAL WITNESS; IHS ENERGY; WILDLIFE CONSERVATION SOCIETY; GLOBAL TRADE ATLAS; U.S. ENERGY INFORMATION ADMINISTRATION

FIGURES BASED ON TRADE VALUE IN U.S. DOLLARS, 2009; CHINA FIGURE EXCLUDES TAIWAN

Women's work in the Toposa village of Namorupus includes making a granary roof from natural materials like grass. Farming falls mainly to women, while caring for and herding cattle to seasonal grazing grounds falls to men.

An SPLA soldier came to Logocho's camp. The soldier's power—of identity in his uniform, of purpose in his weapon—burned itself into the boy's mind. He devised a plan.

on whether to secede from the north and form a fully independent country.

The two sides smile and nod toward the pact, afraid that breaking it will invite international intervention. At the same time they wage a subterranean war of allegation and antagonism. The depths of that duplicity—and the dark prospects for peace—became clear to me midway through my time in Sudan, when half a dozen men in suits accosted me at the airport in Juba, the south's capital. They bundled me into a truck full of soldiers bristling with assault rifles and drove me to a compound in the city. There they took my phone and camera, denied me access to water or a toilet during a day and a night of interrogation. They refused to call the United States Consulate. They were, it turned out, southern Sudanese intelligence agents.

The arrest bewildered me, not just because they wouldn't level any charges but also because their behavior flew against the warmth and goodwill southern Sudanese usually show Westerners. That night, as they released me, a security officer named Gas explained: The intelligence agency had thought I was a spy. "We have been thinking for several weeks that Khartoum might recruit an American," he said. "An American would be perfect, because we allow them to move so freely through our country." I found out later that a driver who had tried to extort money from me had then reported me as a spy, but the incident underscores how deep the suspicion is between north and south.

So the question arises: Amid such animosity, why hasn't the north simply let the south break away? And again the answer is geography. Geography that is now binding them together in a new way: oil. Much of the oil is in the south, but the north, where all the refineries are, controls the distribution of profits.

LOGOCHO DISAPPOINTED HIS FATHER while still in the womb, in a way. Arriving as he did.

A couple of years earlier his mother had delivered twins, and one of them died before Logocho's birth. So according to Murle tradition, he took his dead brother's place, alongside a twin who was stronger, faster. Who loved cows. Who traveled with their father during the dry season instead of staying in the village with the women.

One day when Logocho was nine, his father summoned him. He threatened to withhold the boy's birthright—cows—so Logocho would not

The newly welded framework for a shop takes to the road in Bentiu. The town sits amid the oil fields of Unity State, governed by the south since the end of the civil war. Without a pipeline of its own, the south must send its oil through a northern pipeline to a port on the Red Sea, bound mainly for China.

have a dowry. "If I am alive, you will not get married soon, because you do not like cows."

A sister of Logocho's died of malaria. Another died of dysentery. A disease swept through the cattle—the doom foreseen by the magician, the villagers thought. Then his father died. With the cattle and her husband gone, Logocho's mother despaired. How could she feed her children? She sent Logocho to live with his uncle, who was many miles away and who marveled at the strange child thrust upon him. Who was this useless boy, unable to drive a herd of goats, much less cattle? The uncle yelled and threatened

and raged, and Logocho shrank from him in fear.

Then something remarkable happened. The second civil war had begun, and the SPLA had stopped the great canal-digging machine. One day an SPLA soldier came to Logocho's camp

Logocho and five friends escaped into the wilderness and made their way to an SPLA camp near Boma. Later commanders sent word: Head to Ethiopia. On foot.

looking for food, and the boy gave him some meat. Soldiers had swept through before, and Logocho had sensed the fear in his uncle's voice as he donated a bull to feed them. Now this soldier placed five bullets in Logocho's hand, a reward for his helpfulness. The boy gave three to his uncle, but he held back two for himself, later firing them into the sky from a borrowed gun. The soldier's power—of identity in his uniform, of purpose in his weapon—burned itself into Logocho's mind. He devised a plan and shared it with several of his friends.

When his uncle sent Logocho, who was now 12, out with the animals, he and five friends wandered off, pretending they had discovered a dead buffalo in the bush and wanted to skin it. They escaped into the wilderness, on the run and hungry until they came upon a hunting party of four SPLA soldiers. Two weeks later they made their way into an SPLA camp in the countryside near Boma, assembling with other recruits who wanted to join the rebellion. A handful of grown soldiers lived at the camp, half starved and awaiting orders themselves. For a month the group survived on wild game. Then SPLA commanders sent word: Head to Ethiopia. On foot.

ABOUT THE SAME TIME, in mid-1986, an American named Roger Winter flew to Ethiopia to meet with the SPLA's charismatic leader, John Garang. Winter, in his early 40s, had spent his life working with desperate people. In college he volunteered on the South Side of Chicago, then worked for the Salvation Army, and eventually took a position with the Carter Administration, serving as a sort of human bridge for refugees fleeing oppressive states. Now he headed the nonprofit U.S. Committee for Refugees, personally focusing on crumbling African states such as Rwanda, Ethiopia—and Sudan.

Winter liked Garang, a complicated man. He had a crackling smile and a doctorate from Iowa State, where he had studied economics during the gap between the civil wars. He read Marx and the Bible. His army used child soldiers, yet he had crafted a vision of a unified "New Sudan," with the north and south at peace. And now he wanted to know: Would America help the people of southern Sudan?

Winter felt the place drawing him toward its chaotic heart. He considered himself a human rights worker on a mission to warn the world about coming catastrophes. (He would later

With a constant stream of hucksters and workers lured by the promise of jobs and peace, Juba winks at all comers like a gold rush town. Having grown threefold since 2005, the unruly capital of southern Sudan can barely provide basic city services for its residents.

warn about Rwanda's looming genocide.) What he saw in Sudan shocked him as "a very vicious war," a war that forced any serious observer to make a choice: walk away or get involved. Winter couldn't walk away.

AT THE SPLA OUTPOST Logocho and the other recruits formed a line flanked by the dozen or so soldiers and struck out for Ethiopia. The boys were now solely dependent on the soldiers for food and water. Others joined as they walked, and soon the group numbered more than a hundred, stretched over a mile.

Early in the walk, as hunger set in, the group stopped by a river. Several soldiers lined up on its banks, their rifles raised. One blew a loud whistle, and several animals lifted their heads from the water. The shooters fired a volley toward the flickering ears, killing four hippos. Logocho watched,

As rain greens the land in Burgilo County, men from the Pari tribe will bring their cows home from seasonal grazing camps eight miles away. Until soldiers razed it during the civil war, their village lay at the foot of Lafon Hill (at far right).

"You are young and need to take time here," the soldiers told Logocho. The SPLA used the camp as a kind of recruiting pen, sorting boys according to their age and strength.

their deaths hardly registering against the rumbling of his stomach. The group ate some of the hippo meat on the riverside and dried the rest. Then they continued north toward the border.

After several meals of hippo meat, Logocho's stomach knotted, and his bowels loosened. He remembered his sister who had died of dysentery. It racked him hour after hour, exhausting him, wringing the water from his body. At last he lay down at the side of the path and watched the shapes of passing travelers. Some stopped, but others prodded them forward. "Leave him."

He lay there drying out in the sun, and a thought filled his mind: I am going to die.

A young man named Jowang—a relative of his—saw him. "I will go and get water and come back," he said. A while later someone appeared with water, and Logocho tipped it into his mouth. After some time he climbed to his feet and continued walking. He held on to hope for whatever waited in Ethiopia. Food and water. Rest.

At the end of another day, a soldier made an announcement: A great forest lay ahead, and there was no water in it. To reach water on the other side, they should walk through the night, when the temperature dipped. They entered the trees as darkness settled in, and the men put the boys in the middle of the line and watched for nodding heads.

As they walked, Logocho's own head whipped around. The forest had made a sound. He listened, and it came again, the sound of snapping wood, of something heavy moving in the dark. Then an elephant let out a trumpet that seized the boys where they stood. A blast of gunfire followed, and instructions from a soldier: "Keep walking." And so the night continued, with the terror of elephant charges answered by gunfire.

At daybreak they emerged from the forest, exhausted. The sweat had dried cold on their skin, and they ran forward when they saw a river

ahead. A soldier held up a warning hand. He and others fired their rifles into the water, and several crocodiles glided away. The boys bunched together and paddled through the water as soldiers continually fired around them, and with relief they heaved themselves onto the opposite shore.

Only a little farther now.

"You are still young and need to take time here," the soldiers told Logocho when he first arrived in Ethiopia after the grueling 12-day walk. People had come from all over southern Sudan to this camp near Gambela. It was a camp for refugees, but the SPLA used it as a kind of recruiting pen, sorting boys and men according to their age, strength, and stamina.

LATER, AS ROGER WINTER toured the Ethiopian camps, he peered into boys' faces, and his heart broke for them. They walked on thin legs, some with teeth protruding from shrunken cheeks, others with eyes that bulged, blind from hunger and sickness. He wondered whether he might ever meet any of them again as men.

Many of the boys were malnourished because the northern Sudanese government had learned to use food as a weapon. At first, villagers throughout the south clustered in open areas when they heard planes flying overhead, because pallets of food would always follow. So the government started sending planes in just afterward, dropping bombs. It had a devastating double effect: It streamlined the killing, since a few bombs could wipe out whole crowds of people, and it taught people to fear air-dropped food, so they starved out of sight.

A similar ruthlessness in Darfur would lead the International Criminal Court in The Hague to issue an arrest warrant in March 2009 for Sudan's president, Omar al-Bashir, for war crimes and crimes against humanity. In July 2010 he was also charged with genocide, and a second arrest warrant was issued.

Logocho had hoped to join the fighting force, but he couldn't hold up an AK-47 long enough to train it on a target. So for six months, at the Bonga training camp, he learned other tactical skills, from commando crawling to secret keeping. When John Garang himself came to address the recruits, he delivered a rousing speech, issued uniforms, and divided them into two groups. The larger boys and men could join the fight, and Logocho and the other smaller boys should attend school at the Dima refugee camp, keeping their uniforms at hand.

By the time he was 15, Logocho was finally strong enough to hold a rifle, and he went on a three-week march with other troops to the SPLA stronghold of Kapoeta, near the Uganda-Kenya border. He had looked forward to soldiering, because he had seen the power it held over his domineering uncle. Soon after he arrived at the front line, a report came in of shots fired at a nearby well. Logocho and another young man went to check it out, and they found two of their colleagues shot dead by snipers. As he helped carry one of the bodies, he knew: War was not his purpose. This was not who he was.

Over the next few years Logocho fought as a rebel and dutifully fired his weapon, but he could never bring himself to aim it at another human being. When his friends found wounded Arabs on the battlefield, they would kill them with casual disinterest. Logocho couldn't.

The northern forces had far superior equipment and weaponry. They used jets to bomb southern fuel tanks and troops, so the SPLA fought a guerrilla war in the bush. Each time Logocho's unit moved into new territory, the soldiers each dug a shallow, man-size trench. When they heard the roar of bombers overhead, they dived into the trenches, hoping for the best. The big, Soviet-made Antonov planes arrived with a distinct drone, and then came the whistling of the bombs as they fell. More than once Logocho lay facedown, breathing in the smell of turned earth as his friends died around him.

A Christian friend had shown him a Bible, and one of the stories now made sense. "Woe," Isaiah had said of the place today called Sudan. "Woe to the land shadowed with buzzing wings, which is beyond the rivers of Ethiopia."

BOMBERS CIRCLED OVERHEAD like locusts. Roger Winter knew he had crossed a line. True,

other human rights workers had gone further— one former Irish priest had joined the fight outright, running weapons for the rebels—but the southern Sudanese leadership found in Winter guidance and inspiration. They wanted an American-style revolution, and they saw Winter as their Marquis de Lafayette.

In 1994 the leaders of the SPLA's political wing, the Sudan People's Liberation Movement (SPLM), held their first national convention, under a jungle canopy near the Ugandan border. Khartoum knew about the meeting and had sent planes to bomb it.

Southern leaders had long since abandoned towns and roadways—easy targets for bombs— and taken to the wilderness. Men like Garang and his second in command, Salva Kiir, had grown up in rural cattle camps and felt comfortable in the shelter of the backcountry. More than 500 people made their way to the meeting from across Sudan, and SPLA soldiers moved through the tall grass around the meeting site, combing up the trampled pathways so the bombers couldn't see them. Meeting organizers had cut steps into the hillsides, where the people sat in a naturally camouflaged amphitheater and listened to Winter talk about democracy. After that first, rugged political convention, the SPLM formed a government of its own, with Garang as chairman.

In January I sat with Salva Kiir, who became president of southern Sudan after Garang died in a 2005 helicopter crash, and he seemed uneasy in the presidential office, surrounded by the glitter of central African political power. He wore a black cowboy hat, a gift from President George W. Bush, and was sprawled awkwardly on an ornate sofa as though it cramped him. His political office also pinched him, in a figurative way. He had never expected the presidency to be thrust upon him, he said, and his vision for southern Sudan had him handing it off to someone else. "A peaceful transfer of power," he said, "that's the foundation of a good democracy." He seemed to come alive when I asked about his childhood among the cows, sleeping beside them, suckling them. "Delicious," he said,

Members of southern Sudan's security service bury two colleagues after the brutal intertribal assault on Duk Padiet. Last year conflicts in the south took 2,500 lives and displaced 350,000. Southerners accused the Khartoum government of stirring up violence to destabilize the region.

smiling. Does he still keep cows? "A man never tells how many children or cows he has," he said. "Sometimes you say only one. That one may be ten or a hundred or a thousand." So then how many does he have? He laughed. "One."

IN THE YEARS AFTER THE MEETING in the jungle, Winter continued his preoccupation with southern Sudan, struggling to explain Sudan and America to each other. In southern Sudan people knew little about Western politics; they often called him Senator Roger when he showed up in the bush. Americans knew even less about Sudan. By 2001 Winter had taken a job with the U.S. Agency for International Development, and the war in southern Sudan consumed him.

On the morning of September 11, he was holding a meeting in Washington, D.C., about a possible cease-fire in the Nuba Mountains. Midway

Logocho fought as a rebel and dutifully fired his weapon, but he could never bring himself to aim it at another human being. War was not his purpose. This was not who he was.

the only Americans paying close attention to southern Sudan's troubles were some members of Christian churches. They saw the war as a religious one between Islamic aggressors and non-Muslim victims. September 11 strengthened that view. Church leaders and their congregations put pressure on policymakers in Washington, D.C., to do something in southern Sudan.

Winter knew that the Sudanese civil war was not simply a battle between Islam and Christianity—southern Sudan is in many places a patchwork of animist tribes who know nothing of Christianity. He knew ethnic loyalty meant more than religion. He knew the economics involved, knew the north had suppressed development in the south. He wanted to get more Americans, especially those in Washington, D.C., thinking about Sudan, and he enlisted the help of journalists and legislators.

Where Arabs and black Africans historically had fought over land for grazing, they now fought over oil—as much as three billion barrels, mostly in a disputed borderland between north and south, where tribes and clans had long clashed.

The conflict was complicated, but Winter never discounted the power of religion to be a force for good. He had seen it for himself in 2002.

In a southern Sudanese village called Itti, near the Ethiopian border, he had found a Presbyterian church where more than 300 people crowded under the grass roof each Sunday. They played drums made of animal skins, and Winter was touched by their worship. One Sunday, the young pastor, a man named Simon whom Winter had met briefly before, stepped to the front of the room and spoke about the "peace of God, which passes all understanding," quoting the apostle Paul. Peace even with the Arabs.

Winter thought: This is wisdom personified. After the service he approached the church's

through the meeting, word of that day's terrorist attacks came, with orders to evacuate federal offices. I'm not going anywhere, Winter remembers thinking. We're so close. He had planned to drive to the Sudanese Embassy, but traffic gridlock made that impossible, so he spent the day negotiating on the telephone.

Back in Sudan, something bit him during an around-the-clock push to reach an agreement between the north and the south; he didn't realize it was a snakebite until the next day, when a colleague saw that his purple foot had fang marks.

When the civil war was in its early years,

Arms raised like cattle horns, Jacob Mawich celebrates his victory in the election for leader of a Nuer youth association in Juba. Constituents rejected formal paper ballots and voted in the traditional way by lining up behind their man.

> *Simon looked misplaced in his eyeglasses and smooth-soled, cap-toe shoes. But the villagers waved to him. "Big man!" they called. "I am not the big man," he said, laughing.*

group of elders and asked what he could do to help the congregation. They conferred, while Winter and Simon discussed the possibilities. The elders could ask for anything. A new building. Musical instruments. Food. Medicine. Cash.

Our pastor, Simon, is a smart man, they said. But he has never had a proper education as a pastor. Could you help him?

Winter was stunned. These people hardly had enough to eat, and they chose schooling? Over the next few years he personally paid for Simon to attend a theology school in Kampala, Uganda, taking the young man's word that he would return to the relative bleakness of tiny Itti.

And Winter redoubled his efforts for peace.

READING HIS FRIEND'S BIBLE in an SPLA barracks one night in 1991, Logocho had a realization. Yes, he thought. This is my purpose. He decided that he would become a pastor.

Soon after, a Protestant minister baptized him and asked if he'd like to choose a new name, a new identity. "Yes," Logocho said. "Simon."

He put down his rifle, left the SPLA, and attended a school for refugees in Kenya, where he continued learning English. Then he went to Bible school, and eventually he took a post at the far-flung church in Itti, where a balding American named Roger walked in one Sunday and sat down in the dirt among the other congregants. The young pastor delivered a simple sermon that inspired one of the principal architects of what may become Africa's newest democracy.

Winter's years of diplomatic wrangling culminated with the 2005 pact signed by the north and the south. The chaos and carnage of Sudan's history make it impossible to predict whether the treaty will hold through the 2011 vote on independence. But Winter—along with his U.S. colleagues and negotiators from Kenya, Britain, Norway, and elsewhere—brokered something in Sudan that once seemed impossible: peace. A peace that has held for five years.

SIMON WALKED WITH ME recently in Itti. He enjoys no social standing, since he has no cows, and he looked misplaced in his eyeglasses and smooth-soled, cap-toe shoes. For the past three years he has earned income during the week doing community outreach for the Wildlife Conservation Society—a long way, in a sense, from the cattle camps and hunting parties of his peers. But the villagers waved to him, and they promised to

see him Sunday morning. "Big man!" they called.

"I am not the big man," he said, laughing.

Simon could have stayed in Uganda or gone to Kenya. Like the famous Lost Boys, he could have emigrated to America, where he could have made a better living. Why not go to the U.S.? He smiled and, as is his habit, made a small clicking sound by pulling his tongue back from the gap in his grin.

"No," he said.

As a child, Logocho had left behind the pastoral tradition. He had come of age in the chaos and pain of war, and then, when he became

The connection between a Dinka man and his cow is profound; it is part of his personal identity. The matter of a southern Sudanese national identity is on the table as leaders prepare for next year's referendum on independence, when they hope to persuade Dinka, Nuer, and other feuding tribes to unify.

Simon, he had used his faith to reach an influential American who offered him and his country support. His history was the history of southern Sudan, and his purpose its people.

"No," he said. "This is my place." ☐

3Degrees of Japan's Seas

The waters off the coast vary from frigid to temperate to tropical. The marine life is uniformly extraordinary.

Hunting for morsels of plankton, a school of spadefish hovers near the surface off Japan's subtropical Bonin Islands. The turquoise color permeates the water late in the afternoon, as the red rays of the setting sun spread out and grow weak.

Seventy miles southwest of
Tokyo, a moray eel slithers
through the branches of a
soft coral in the cool waters
of Suruga Bay. Deep and
narrow, the bay plummets
more than 8,000 feet.

The photographer's assistant hangs on to part of an ice canopy that can reach a thickness of 25 feet in winter, blanketing Shire-toko Peninsula waters. A decade ago these seas were icebound an average of 90 days a year. Today the span is about 65 days.

Sunlight streams between cracks in the ice. Thicker chunks glow emerald green, bejeweled by algae. The characters of this frosty realm begin to appear: a translucent, blue swimming snail, a pink fish with a tail like a geisha's fan, a bright orange lumpsucker that looks as if it leaped out of a Pokémon cartoon. This is the underwater world that awaits photographer Brian Skerry, who is lumbering across the beach near a fishing town called Rausu, in Japan's northeastern corner. Wearing a hooded dry suit and carrying an air tank, hoses, regulator, and 32 pounds of weights, he pulls on his fins and slowly submerges his face to get used to the 29°F water. His lips go numb. And then, camera in hand, Skerry dives between the ice floes into the waters of the Sea of Okhotsk, bordering the Shiretoko Peninsula.

Most people think of Japan as a compact collection of large islands, but a map of the country shows otherwise. Japan stretches over 1,500 miles and includes more than 5,000 islands. As land mingles with sea over these vast distances, it embraces at least three distinct ecosystems. In the frigid north, sea-eagles, with their seven-foot wingspans, and king crabs frequent the ice-covered seas off the remote Shiretoko Peninsula. In the mild central waters of the Izu Peninsula and Toyama Bay, a few hours' drive from the skyscrapers of Tokyo, firefly squid swarm, and soft coral forests grow. In the balmy south, delicate butterflyfish and huge sand tiger sharks share coral reefs in the Bonin Islands, a collection of 30 or more islands about 500 miles south of Tokyo.

Ocean currents are key to the marine diversity, bathing Japan's shores in temperatures of water that range from around 30°F to 85°F. The currents also bring the country a couple of world records. The powerful Kuroshio shoots warm water northward, allowing coral reefs to thrive where they would not normally be found. The East Sakhalin Current draws cold water down toward Japan, helping make the Shiretoko Peninsula the southernmost spot with winter sea ice.

These currents control more than water temperature. They transport distant marine life as well. Inlets pockmark Japan's volcanic shoreline, explains Florida Institute of Technology professor Robert van Woesik. On islands surrounded by coral reefs, the lagoons "act like baseball mitts catching coral and fish larvae."

As in so much of the world's oceans, these ecosystems are at risk. Japan is filling in lagoons to create more land to build upon. When this happens, fish, coral, and crab larvae glide past without settling down.

For now, the array of ocean life is thriving, as Brian Skerry's photographs show. When he surfaces from the frigid waters, he's grateful for the teahouse on the beach. Stripped of his gear, he warms up by sipping miso soup as he sits on the floor watching the snow fall. All the while, the orange lumpsucker swims, and the ice glows green undersea. —*Juli Berwald*

A contributor to the magazine since 1998, photojournalist and veteran diver Brian Skerry is the author of Face to Face With Manatees.

JAPAN'S SWIRLING SEAS

Warm and cold ocean currents collide off the coast of Japan, creating a wide range of temperatures. The result is a series of strikingly different marine communities, swept in by the currents.

Sea surface temperature

ARCTIC	TEMPERATURE	TROPICAL
29°F	57°	85°

East Sakhalin and Oyashio currents
These currents pull cold water from northern latitudes toward Japan.

SIBERIA

Sea of Okhotsk

150°

140°E

East Sakhalin Current

SAKHALIN

(Russia)

RUSSIA

50°

Russian-administered islands claimed by Japan

Shiretoko Peninsula
Rausu

KURIL ISLANDS

Oyashio current

HOKKAIDO
• Sapporo

Warm-core eddy

CHINA

NORTH KOREA

Pyongyang

40°N

Sea of Japan (East Sea)

J A P A N

Toyama Bay

Cold-core eddy

Yellow Sea

Seoul

SOUTH KOREA

H O N S H U

Tokyo ★

Eddies
Where currents collide, nutrients from cold water feed warm-water phytoplankton. The result is a spinning buffet for fish.

Korea Strait

Kyoto •

Suruga Bay

Izu Peninsula

current

KYUSHU *SHIKOKU*

Kuroshio

Izu Islands

30°

East China Sea

RYUKYU ISLANDS

Kuroshio current
Reaching five miles an hour or more, this deep, powerful current ferries warm waters northward along Japan's coast.

PACIFIC OCEAN

Bonin Islands

Okinawa

Philippine Sea

Iriomote

0 mi   100
0 km   100

VIRGINIA W. MASON, NGM STAFF
SOURCE: GEOPHYSICAL FLUID DYNAMICS LABORATORY, NOAA

SEA SURFACE TEMPERATURE IS A COMPUTER SIMULATION FOR A SINGLE DAY IN DECEMBER.

The keen eyes of a Steller's sea-eagle (left) seek the flash of herring between ice floes off the Shiretoko Peninsula. Underneath the ice, spikes meet spikes as an Alaska king crab the size of a nickel crawls over a knobby sea star. After a dozen years, the crustacean will grow to the size of a tractor tire.

140°E
Shiretoko Peninsula
— 44°N
HOKKAIDO

JAPAN
★Tokyo

North Central South

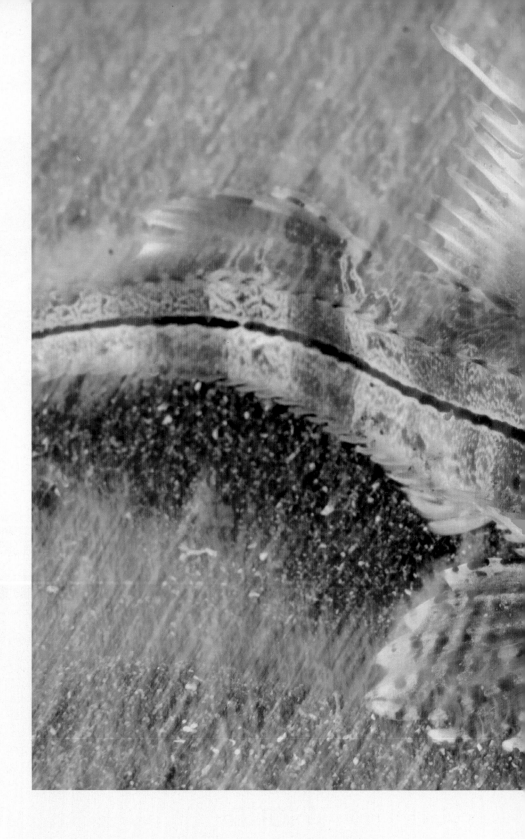

In the shallow waters off Hokkaido, a barbed poacher crawls across glistening volcanic sand on spiny pectoral fins. Only the females of this cold-water fish sport a distinctive Pinocchio-like snout.

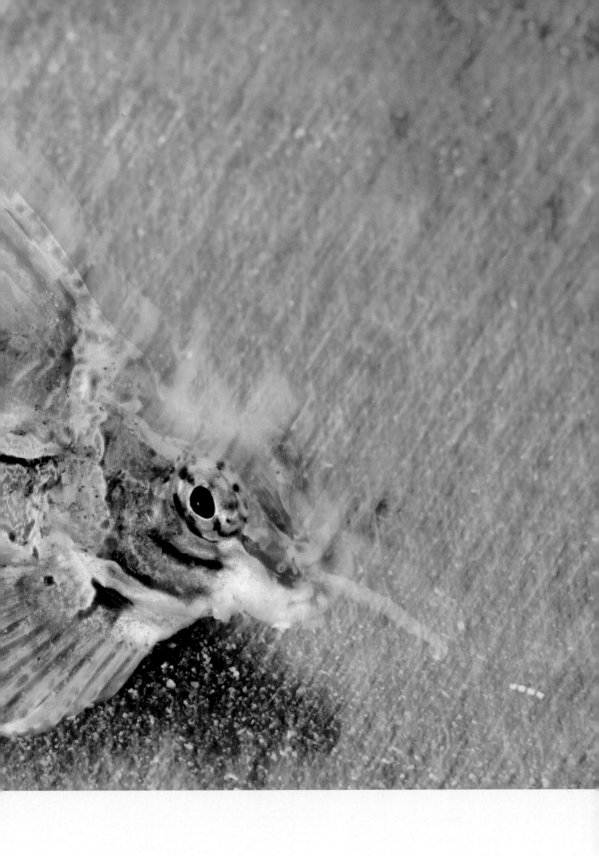

A volcanic beach off Toyama Bay glows electric blue (left). The light comes from female firefly squid, which spawn in spring, then die and wash ashore, their tentacles lit like millions of aquamarine LEDs. Off the Izu Peninsula, a yellow goby peers through the window of its corroded soda-can home, evidence of the 127 million people just above the water's surface.

140°E

Toyama Bay

JAPAN

★Tokyo

—35°N

Izu
Suruga Peninsula
Bay

NorthCentralSouth

What looks like a tangle of gnarled cables is in fact a forest of deep-water whip coral in Suruga Bay. Each strand is studded with feeding polyps that reach tiny tentacles into the currents to grab floating food.

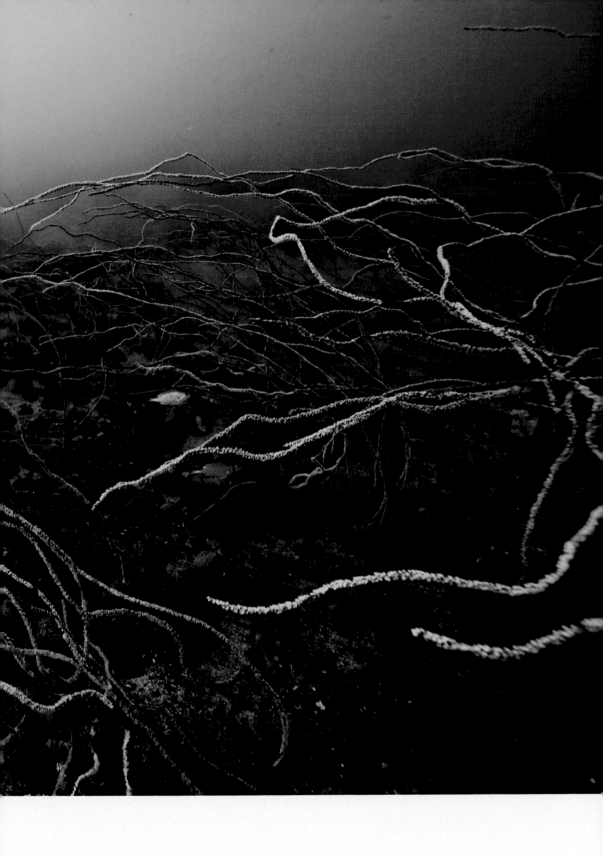

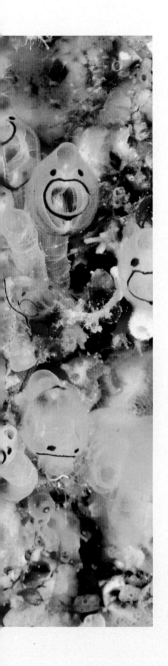

Purple tunicates (left) filter the water for food. They have no scientific name and live behind a single rock in a cave off Chichi-shima island. The wrought iron butterflyfish (above) pauses for a wrasse fish to clean its skin. The Japanese have long been intrigued by the similarity between the butterflyfish's black-and-white motif and the patterns on a samurai kimono.

140°E

J A P A N

★Tokyo

27°N — Chichi-shima
Bonin Islands

North Central **South**

A sand tiger shark off the Bonin Islands will soon give birth. During the nine-month pregnancy, the largest two pups will have eaten their siblings for sustenance, a kind of cannibalism unique to this species.

NBURYING THE AZTEC

THE EXCAVATION OF A SACRED PYRAMID IS TURNING UP CLUES TO THE EMPIRE'S BLOODY RITUALS—BUT SO FAR, NO SIGN OF ITS MOST FEARED EMPEROR.

BY ROBERT DRAPER

PHOTOGRAPHS BY KENNETH GARRETT AND JESÚS LÓPEZ

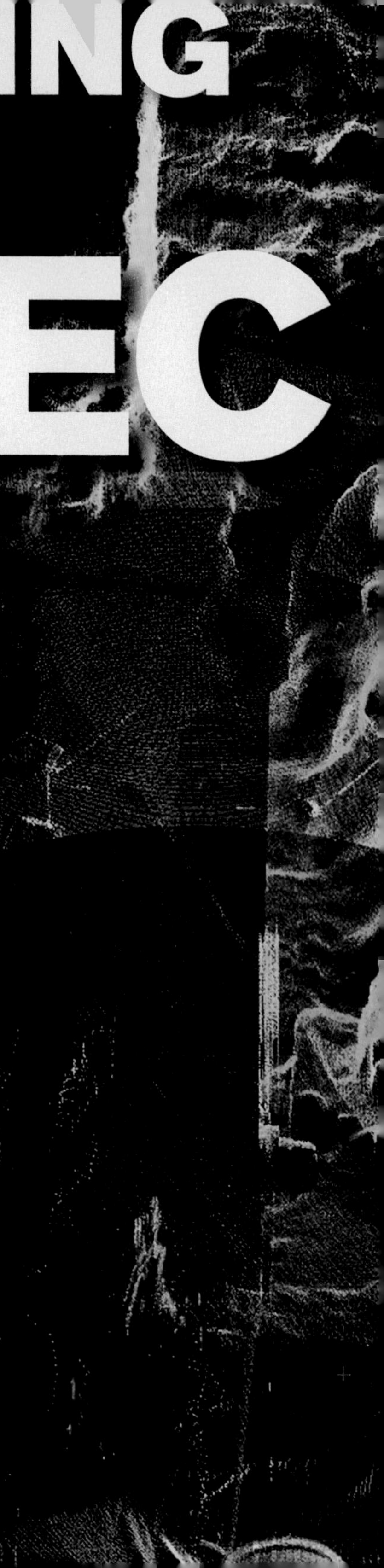

Archaeologists used laser-driven pulses of light to produce a green 3-D image of a fractured stone depicting an Aztec earth goddess. In a shaft near her head lay six offerings of artifacts (see art, page 122).

GUIDO GALVANI AND MARÍA SÁNCHEZ VEGA, COURTESY TEMPLO MAYOR PROJECT, NATIONAL INSTITUTE OF ANTHROPOLOGY AND HISTORY, MEXICO

In May a team of 30 technicians and two cranes took 15 hours to move the 12-ton stone of the earth goddess Tlaltecuhtli, broken into four pieces, about 500 feet from the excavation site to a new home in Mexico City's Templo Mayor Museum. A two-and-a-half-year restoration process has revealed traces of the andesite stone's original ocher, red, blue, white, and black pigments— but not the missing center of the monolith.

KENNETH GARRETT

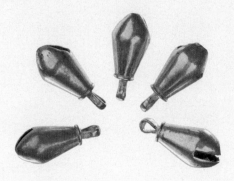

ON THE EDGE OF MEXICO CITY'S FAMED ZÓCALO PLAZA,

next to the ruins of the Aztec sacred pyramid known as the Templo Mayor, the remains of an animal—perhaps a dog or a wolf—were discovered. It had been dead for 500 years and lay in a stone-lined shaft eight feet deep. It is likely the animal had no name, nor an owner. Yet the anonymous canine had evidently meant something to someone. It wore a collar made of jade beads and turquoise plugs in its ears. From its ankles dangled bracelets with little bells of pure gold.

The archaeological team, led by Leonardo López Luján, unearthed the so-called Aristo-Canine in the summer of 2008, two years into an excavation that began when foundation work for a new building revealed an astonishing object. It was a 12-ton rectangular monolith made of pinkish andesite stone, broken into four large pieces, bearing the mesmerizingly horrific likeness of the earth goddess Tlaltecuhtli (pronounced tlal-TEK-tli)—the symbol of the Aztec life and death cycle, squatting to give birth while drinking her own blood, devouring her own creation. It was the third flat Aztec monolith to be discovered by accident in the vicinity of the Templo Mayor, along with a 24-ton black basalt Sun Stone (excavated in 1790) and an 8-ton Disk of Coyolxauhqui, the moon goddess (1978).

After years of painstaking excavation, López Luján and his crew have discovered, in a deep pit beside the monolith, some of the most exotic Aztec offerings ever found. Removing a stucco patch in the plaza floor, the excavators came upon 21 white flint sacrificial knives painted red: the teeth and gums of the Aztec earth monster, her mouth open wide to receive the dead. They dug deeper and found a bundle wrapped in agave leaves. It contained an assortment of sacrificial perforators made of jaguar bone, used by Aztec priests to spill their own blood as a gift to the gods. Alongside the perforators were bars of copal—priestly incense, another spiritual purifier. The perforators and incense were carefully arranged inside the bundle, along with feathers and jade beads.

To López Luján's surprise, several feet underneath this bundle lay a second offering, this one

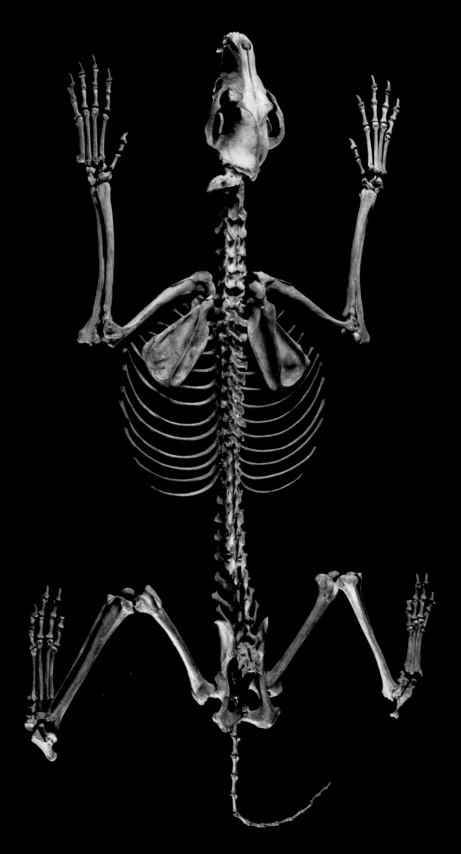

Its skeleton reassembled for museum display, the animal known as the
Aristo-Canine wore a seashell belt and gold bells (opposite) on its hind legs.

An aerial view over Mexico City shows remnants of ancient Tenochtitlan visible around the green awnings of the Templo Mayor excavation site (opposite, lower left). Archaeologists, including Ángel González (below), have already recovered tens of thousands of artifacts that will help scholars decode the Aztec view of the universe. The search for a royal tomb has moved to a new tunnel just west of the site.

in a stone box. It held the skeletons of two golden eagles—symbols of the sun—with their bodies facing westward. Surrounding the eagles were 27 sacrificial knives, 24 of them dressed up in fur and other costumes, like raggedy puppets, to represent deities associated with the setting sun. By last January, the team had uncovered a total of six offerings in the shaft—the last one 24 feet below street level and containing a ceramic jar filled with 310 greenstone beads, earplugs, and figurines. The placement of every excavated object appeared to be governed by an exquisite logic, re-creating the Aztec Empire's entire cosmology.

It was at the very bottom of the second offering box that López Luján encountered the elaborately ornamented animal. Covering it were seashells and the remains of clams, crabs, and snails—creatures brought to this spot from the Gulf of Mexico, and the Atlantic and Pacific Oceans. In Aztec cosmology, López Luján knew, this tableau suggested the first level of the underworld, with the canine serving to guide its master's soul across a dangerous river.

But which human soul? Since the Spaniard Hernán Cortés's conquest of Mexico in 1521, no Aztec emperor's remains have been discovered. Yet historical records say that three Aztec rulers were cremated and their ashes buried at the foot of the Templo Mayor. When the Tlaltecuhtli monolith was found, López Luján noticed that

the god depicted held a rabbit, with ten dots above it, in its clawed right foot. In the Aztec writing system, 10-Rabbit is 1502—the year, according to the codices surviving from the era, that the empire's most feared ruler, Ahuitzotl (pronounced ah-wee-tzohtl), was laid to rest amid great ceremony.

López Luján is convinced that Ahuitzotl's burial place is somewhere near where the monolith was found. If he is right, then the Aristo-Canine may be a subterranean guide into the mystique of a people we know as the Aztec, but who called themselves Mexica (pronounced meh-shee-ka), and whose legacy forms the core of the Mexican identity. If López Luján finds Ahuitzotl's tomb, it will be the culmination of a

remarkable 32-year inquiry into one of the most mythologized and misunderstood empires in the Western Hemisphere. Alas, little is certain when it comes to the Aztec Empire—a reign simultaneously brutal and complex, brief and literally paved over, yet manifestly prominent in a nation's consciousness a half millennium later.

"PAST IS PRESENT everywhere in Mexico," says López Luján. That is especially true of the Aztec Empire, virtually all of which resides just beneath the footsteps of a modern nation.

When word spread in 1978 that the Templo Mayor had been firmly located in the heart of the world's second most populous city, the resulting spectacle was *(Continued on page 130)*

Red, white, and green lights illuminate the ruins of the Templo Mayor for nighttime visitors. Digs have revealed 13 phases of construction from 1375 to 1519, including the pyramid's double staircases.

Iztaccíhuatl

Popocatépetl

Reflection of the Cosmos

The Aztec imagined the universe as a plot of land surrounded by water, with a vertical axis linking 13 heavens and 9 levels of the underworld. Tenochtitlan's grid may have been modeled on that cosmic order.

Lake Chalco

Lake Xochimilco

Lake Texcoco

Dike

AREA ENLARGED

Road to Ixtapalapan

Tlatelolco

Tenochtitlan

Aqueduct

(N)

TEMPLO MAYOR

AN AZTEC ISLAND HOME

Aztec rulers built a powerful city-state on an island in Lake Texcoco in the Basin of Mexico. Called Tenochtitlan, it was divided by long avenues, crisscrossed by canals, and connected to the mainland by causeways. At its heart was the Sacred Precinct, the empire's religious center, anchored by the Templo Mayor, which was built to unite sky, earth, and worlds below.

Sacred Precinct

Religious rituals and civic life in the city of 200,000 converged on a 30-acre plaza. Inside its walls, shrines and racks of enemy skulls stood in the shadow of the Templo Mayor. The plaza also contained smaller pyramids, schools for nobles, and a ball court.

Triple Alliance
- Texcoco
- Tenochtitlan (Present-day Mexico City)
- Tlacopan

Extent of Ahuitzotl's Aztec Empire

Enemy state

NORTH AMERICA

AREA ENLARGED

SOUTH AMERICA

0 mi 100
0 km 100

AZTEC RULERS

Tenochtitlan is founded in 1325. Over the centuries only 11 men rule as *tlatoani*, each with a unique name glyph.

ACAMAPICHTLI (Handful of Arrows) is the first tlatoani, hereditary ruler of the Aztec city-state.

1325

1375

1337 The market town of Tlatelolco grows north of Tenochtitlan.

1350 Causeways and canals link Tenochtitlan's neighborhoods.

Templo Mayor

A ceremonial theater, the stepped pyramid was topped by two small temples to honor rain god Tlaloc and Huitzilopochtli, god of sun and war. The pyramid towered 150 feet tall.

Shrine to Huitzilopochtli

Shrine to Tlaloc

Ritual Sacrifice

Spilling human blood, priests frequently reenacted the death of goddess Coyolxauhqui at the hands of her brother, Huitzilopochtli—a mythic battle between night and day, female and male.

Coyolxauhqui

DETAIL ON NEXT PAGE

Serpent Sculptures

The base of the pyramid was ornamented with sculptures of snakes, linking it to mythical Coatepec—"hill of serpents," a sacred place.

Tlaltecuhtli Stone

Found at the foot of the pyramid, the monolith of the earth goddess was carved of pink andesite quarried six miles away and transported by 200 to 500 men with ropes, poles, and perhaps a balsa raft.

SACRED PRECINCT

Scene depicted circa 1500.

HUITZILIHUITL (Hummingbird Feather) marries into two rival royal families, cementing alliances.

CHIMALPOPOCA (Smoking Shield) survives ten years before he is murdered by a rival.

ITZCOATL (Obsidian Snake) joins leaders of Tlacopan and Texcoco in mobilizing a new empire.

1395

1396 Huitzilihuitl makes alliances and expands the capital.

1417

1427

1427-1430 An alliance led by Tenochtitlan wins control of central Mexico.

1440

Earth, Sun, Moon

The largest Aztec monolith yet discovered, the 12-ton earth goddess stone is shown with original red, ocher, blue, white, and black pigments.

Tlaltecuhtli Stone (Earth Goddess)
Found 2006

13.7 x 11.9 ft

Sun Stone
1790

11.7 ft

Disk of Coyolxauhqui (Moon Goddess)
1978

10.6 x 10.1 ft

Offering 121

Almost seven feet below the monolith itself was offering 126 (photo, pages 127-9), the largest cache of artifacts found to date and a fitting tribute to Tlaltecuhtli's fertile, feminine nature.

DETAIL OF OFFERING 125

The offerings in the shaft seem to mark a gateway to Earth's center, rather than to a burial spot, as first thought. The search for royal tombs continues.

Offering 127

Offering 128

Offering 129

Offering 131

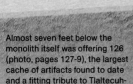

OFFERINGS TO THE GODS

Beneath the Tlaltecuhtli monolith and in a deep shaft beside it, archaeologists unearthed many offerings, filled with animals, plants, and objects of gold, jade, copper, turquoise, and flint, brought to the temple from all realms of the empire. The Aztec buried objects to worship the gods—a symbolic ritual archaeologists are still decoding.

MOCTEZUMA ILHUICAMINA (Angry Lord, He Shoots the Sky) expands the empire using elite warriors, including "eagle lords."

AXAYACATL (Water Face) attacks the Tarascan people but loses the war and 20,000 men.

TIZOC (Chalk Leg), brother to Axayacatl and Ahuitzotl, rules weakly and is assassinated.

1440

1469

1481

1486

1450-54 Floods, then severe drought and famine, plague the Basin of Mexico.

1473 Tenochtitlan subjugates Tlatelolco and rises to dominant city-state.

1487 Templo Mayor is rededicated with the blood of thousands.

Buried Meaning

The spatial arrangement of the complex contents of offering box 125 provides clues to a mystery: Were the artifacts layered to represent a soul's journey to Mictlan, the underworld?

LEVEL 1

The top layer contained gold bells, a spider monkey pelt, jade and gold ornaments, and golden eagles wearing copper.

The eagles faced west, toward the setting sun. Nocturnal power was signified by eight knives "dressed" as lunar deities.

LEVEL 2

A layer of 62 marine species from the Atlantic and Pacific included crabs, clams, snails, sea urchins, and corals.

The abundant sea life may represent dangerous waters the dead must cross, trekking through nine levels of obstacles.

LEVEL 3

In the last layer, an aged female dog or wolf wore a jade necklace, olive shell belt, and turquoise earplugs.

Perhaps the jewelry signified a royal pet assigned to guide and protect its master on the dark odyssey.

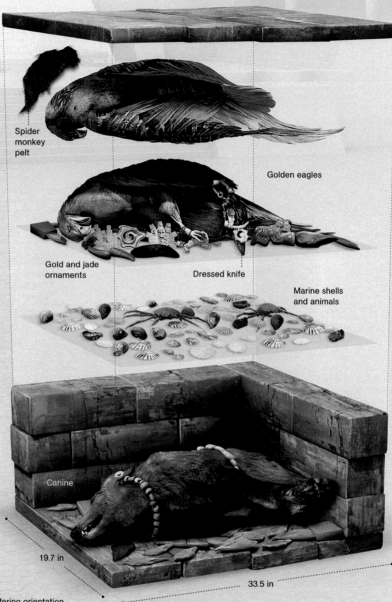

Spider monkey pelt

Golden eagles

Gold and jade ornaments

Dressed knife

Marine shells and animals

Canine

19.7 in

33.5 in

N Offering orientation

ALEJANDRO TUMAS; SHELLEY SPERRY
ART: HERNÁN CAÑELLAS. MAP: MAGGIE SMITH

SOURCES: LEONARDO LÓPEZ LUJÁN, TEMPLO MAYOR PROJECT, INAH; FRANCES F. BERDAN, CALIFORNIA STATE UNIVERSITY, SAN BERNARDINO; JULIANA NOVIC AND MICHAEL E. SMITH, ARIZONA STATE UNIVERSITY; EMILY UMBERGER, UNIVERSITY OF ARIZONA

AHUITZOTL (Water Beast) conquers new lands and is called *huey tlatoani*, or great speaker.

MOCTEZUMA XOCOYOTZIN (Angry Lord, the Younger) aggressively moves to consolidate his empire, largest in Mesoamerica's history.

CUITLAHUAC (Excrement) rules only 80 days before succumbing to smallpox.

CUAUHTEMOC (Descending Eagle)—the last emperor—is captured, tortured, and hanged by Cortés.

1502

1520

1500 Heavy rains in poorly built aqueduct flood Tenochtitlan.

1499-1506 Drought and famine plague the Basin of Mexico.

1519 Cortés enlists native city-states to destroy the empire.

1521 Smallpox begins to ravage the basin's million inhabitants.

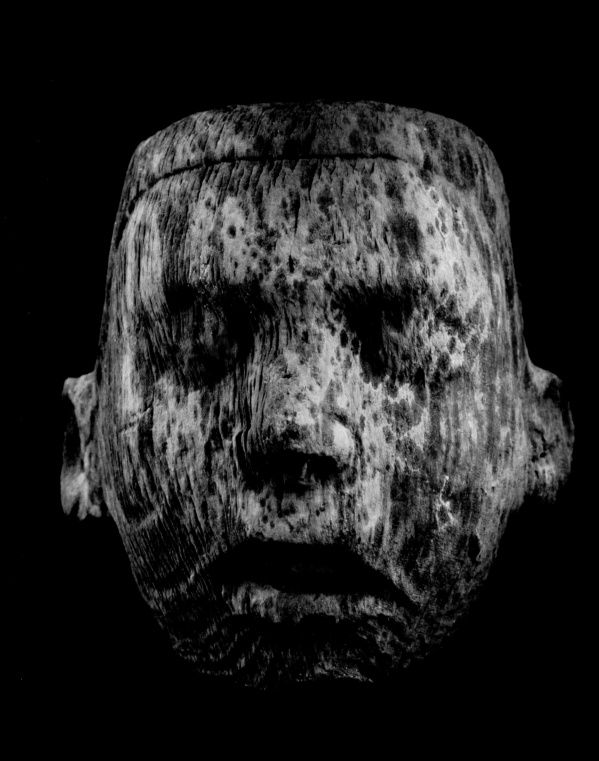

Inside the shaft beside the monolith, archaeologists found offering box 125, depicting what project leader López Luján calls a "miniature image of the universe." Among the treasures offered to the gods were a gold ornament (left, top), a greenstone necklace (left, bottom), and flint and copal knives (above). Directly under Tlaltecuhtli, the largest offering yet unearthed (box 126, following pages, and drawing below) held a tiny pine mask (far left, and 5 below), and 8,500 animal bones (7). Other objects in the box: sacrificial knives (1, 2, 11), shells and corals (3, 4, 12, 13), a sawfish bill (6), a jar of grain (8), a scepter (9), and fire god sculptures (10).

(*Continued from page 117*) more like a Broadway opening than an archaeological triumph. Jimmy Carter, François Mitterrand, Gabriel García Márquez, Jacques Cousteau, and Jane Fonda were among the dozens of celebrities who were treated to a tour of the dig site, some by Mexico's President José López Portillo, whose controversial decision to raze 13 buildings had made the excavation possible. And now it is happening again, with news circulating that one or more rulers may be entombed underneath the Zócalo's periphery. Today López Luján spends an inordinate amount of time chaperoning VIPs through the cramped and shrouded excavation site on the western edge of the pyramid. The Mexican press responds in droves to the latest archaeological revelations. Ordinary folks rap on the secure entrance to ask for a look; López Luján often obliges. The round-faced, good-humored, 46-year-old scholar understands the psychic pull. "Right now Mexicans realize they are living in a tragic present," he says. "But the past gives the people a way of saying they're somebody."

Unlike the Maya, Mesoamerica's other pre-Columbian powerhouse, the Aztec are exclusively identified with Mexico, and today it spares no opportunity to mythologize them. In the center of the Mexican flag is the Aztec eagle, which is also incorporated into the logos of the nation's two main airlines. There is Banco Azteca and TV Azteca, and the national soccer team wears uniforms featuring the iconic eagle and plays its home games in Estadio Azteca. And of course Mexico City itself—the nerve center of the nation—is an implicit homage to the city-state of Tenochtitlan and to Aztec indomitability.

But to see the Aztec in strictly iconic terms is to misunderstand them. To begin with, the mighty Aztec sustained their empire—the triple alliance of Tenochtitlan, Texcoco, and Tlacopan—for less than a century before it was eviscerated by

---

Robert Draper is a contributing writer for National Geographic. *Kenneth Garrett frequently photographs archaeology stories for the magazine. Photographer Jesús López lives in Mexico City.*

European conquerors. For all the fear and loathing the rulers instilled in conquered regions, their dominion was ephemeral. They did not erect temples and disseminate cultural traditions across the countryside as the ancient Romans or Inca did. Instead, the Aztec maintained what some scholars call "a cheap empire," one in which the conquered were permitted to continue governing themselves so long as they ponied up tributary objects—a protection scheme buttressed by periodic shows of force. The Aztec chose to express their ingenuity largely in the epicenter of Tenochtitlan. Yet the great city was in many ways a repository of customs, images, and spiritual practices borrowed from previous civilizations. As López Luján's father, the Mesoamerican scholar Alfredo López Austin, puts it, "The most common misconception is that the Aztec were a completely original culture. They weren't."

But the harsh caricature of the Aztec as bloodthirsty is just as misguided. So grossly did the conquering Spaniards overstate the Mexica bloodlust—claiming, for example, that 80,400 humans were put to death at a single temple dedication, a feat that would have depopulated much of central Mexico—that some groups today feel justified in dismissing sacrifice as a European fiction. That's going too far. Chemical examinations during the past 15 years of porous surfaces throughout Mexico City reveal "blood traces everywhere," says López Luján. "You have the sacrificial stones, the sacrificial knives, the bodies of 127 victims—you can't deny the human sacrifice."

But, he is quick to add, you'll find human sacrifice everywhere in the world at that time. The Maya and numerous other cultures predated the Aztec's embrace of the practice. "It isn't the violence of a people but rather of an age—a warlike atmosphere when the religions of the time demanded that humans be sacrificed to replenish the gods," observes López Austin. And that spiritual imperative was received by the Aztec people with considerable anguish, according to analyses of codices by Harvard historian of religions Davíd Carrasco. "They were upset about sacrifice," he says. "I think there are a lot of signs that they were bothered by it."

The codices reveal that this was a people with a sophisticated awareness of the limitations of an empire that relied on human sacrifice. Even as they achieved their greatest might under Ahuitzotl, the predicate for their doom was being laid. A people who believed themselves at the center of a highly precarious universe were also inflicted with what Carrasco terms a "cosmic insecurity."

THE EMPIRE BEGAN from scratch. The first Aztec, or Mexica, migrated from the north—from Aztlan, so it was said, though this ancestral homeland has never been located and perhaps existed only in legend. They spoke the Nahuatl tongue of the mighty Toltec, whose dominance across central Mexico had ended in the 12th century. But language was the Mexica's only connection to greatness. Chased off from one Basin of Mexico settlement after another, they at last happened upon an island in Lake Texcoco that no one else wanted and in 1325 proclaimed it Tenochtitlan. Little more than a swamp, Tenochtitlan lacked drinkable water and stones and wood for building. But its scruffy new inhabitants, though "almost totally uncultured," as renowned scholar Miguel León-Portilla puts it, compensated with what he terms "an indomitable will."

These settlers proceeded to dig through the ruins of the once great city-states of Teotihuacan and Tula. What they saw, they appropriated. By 1430 Tenochtitlan had become greater than either city, a marvel of landfill and aqueducts, divided by canals and causeways into four quadrants all in orbit around the centerpiece of a double-staircased pyramid with twin temples at its summit. None of their flourishes was particularly original, and that was the point. The Mexica sought to establish ancestral connections with empires past—particularly through the machinations of Tlacaelel, the royal consigliere who could boast that "none of the past kings has acted without my opinion or counsel." During the first half of the 15th century, Tlacaelel introduced a new version of Mexica history, asserting that

his people were offspring of the great Toltec and elevating Huitzilopochtli—their patron god of the sun and of war—to the pantheon of exalted Toltec deities. The royal counselor went one step further. As Miguel León-Portilla writes, Tlacaelel crafted their imperial destiny as "the conquest of all other nations…to capture victims for sacrifice, because the source of all life, the sun, would die unless it were fed with human blood."

Thus did the reviled newcomers from the north ascend to nobility. They subjugated town after town in the Basin of Mexico. Under Moctezuma I, in the late 1440s, the Mexica and their allies marched over 200 miles to extend their empire southward into the present-day states of

BELIEVING THEY LIVED IN A HIGHLY PRECARIOUS UNIVERSE INFLICTED THE AZTEC WITH A COSMIC INSECURITY.

Morelos and Guerrero. By the 1450s they had pushed into the northern Gulf coast. And by 1465 the Chalco Confederacy, the lone holdout in the Basin of Mexico, was vanquished.

It would fall to the eighth Aztec ruler, Ahuitzotl, to stretch the empire to its breaking point.

HE DOES NOT HAVE A FACE. The man whose remains Leonardo López Luján hopes to find near the Templo Mayor is not represented in any artwork. "The only images we have of an Aztec ruler are of Moctezuma II, and these were made based on descriptions from the Spaniards after his death," López Luján says, referring to the last emperor who ruled over Mexico on the eve of the Spanish conquest. "About Moctezuma II, we have many details of his life. Of Ahuitzotl, we have very few."

Here's what we do know: The high-ranking military officer assumed the throne in 1486 after his brother Tizoc lost control of the empire and

Ahuitzotl's funerary bundle, in
turquoise diadem and mask, was
carried to his pyre by nobles.

perished—perhaps by poison, perhaps by his younger brother's hand. His very name connoted violence; in Nahuatl parlance, the *ahuitzotl* was a vicious otter-like being that could throttle humans with its muscular tail. Ahuitzotl's 45 conquests, the hallmark of his 16-year reign, were all colorfully memorialized in a Spanish viceroy's manuscript known as the Codex Mendoza. His armies conquered swaths along the Pacific coast, down into present-day Guatemala—and thus "expanded the empire's territorial reach to unprecedented limits," according to Carrasco. Some of these battles were purely exhibits of supremacy or to punish recalcitrant local leaders. The majority were to fulfill two bedrock lusts: tributary goods for Tenochtitlan and victims for the gods.

The first rule of Aztec dominion was well in place by the time Ahuitzotl acquired power: Take the conquered region's best stuff. "The merchants and traders played the roles of spies," explains Eduardo Matos Moctezuma, the archaeologist who oversaw the massive excavations at the Templo Mayor that began in 1978. Once they reported back about the resources a town possessed, the imperial forces would prepare their attack. "The military expansion was an economic expansion," says Matos Moctezuma. "The Aztec didn't impose their religion. They just wanted the products."

Not even gold held as much significance among the Mesoamerican peoples as jade, which represented fertility—and which in Central America could be found only in the mines of Guatemala. Unsurprisingly then, Ahuitzotl established trade routes into those lands—acquiring not only the metamorphic green stones but also, says López Luján, "quetzal feathers, gold, jaguar skins, and cacao, which was their money that grew on trees." With this abundance of riches, Tenochtitlan became a mercantile powerhouse as well as a cultural one—"the richest art center at that time, as Paris and New York would be later," says López Luján.

The Aztec bling became part of the ornately ritualized spirituality of Tenochtitlan. The Templo Mayor was not simply a burial pyramid like those erected by the ancient Egyptians but rather the symbol of the sacred mountain of Coatepec. The mountain was the site of a cosmological soap opera: The newly born sun god Huitzilopochtli slew his warrior sister, the moon goddess Coyolxauhqui, and flung her to the bottom of the mountain. With regular doses of such sacrificed warriors, the Mexica believed, the gods would be sated and the life cycle would go on. Without such sacrifices, the gods would perish and the world would end. "The sacred mountain is as important as the cross in Christianity," says Carrasco. For the Mexica, as for most Mesoamerican cultures, "there was this repetitive destruction and creation."

MOST OF THE BATTLES WERE FOUGHT TO FULFILL TWO BEDROCK LUSTS: TRIBUTARY GOODS AND VICTIMS FOR THE GODS.

Paying homage to the sacred mountain meant marching colorfully garbed captive soldiers up the stairs of the pyramid, forcing them to perform ceremonial dances, and then cutting out their hearts and rolling their corpses down the steps. Rounding up the requisite prisoners to be sacrificed later was an ongoing campaign. Ritual battles were staged on specific days, on neutral land, with the explicit purpose of capturing prisoners, not territory. As the Aztec scholar Ross Hassig notes, each war "was formally initiated by burning a large pyre of paper and incense between the two armies." The Mexica did not speak of "holy wars," because for them there was no other kind. Combat and religion were inseparable.

IN HIS VERY FIRST CAMPAIGN, Ahuitzotl led his army through several cities to the northeast to gather victims for his coronation rites in Tenochtitlan. Annoyed that several enemy lords failed to attend his crowning, the new ruler undertook a second series of invasions in 1487, pillaging the towns of the Huaxtec region and seizing an immense number of captives. Ahuitzotl's adversaries got the message. This time their leaders were well represented at the dedication of the Templo Mayor, and they watched in horrified amazement as the sacrificial victims they had surrendered were slaughtered in vast numbers by ritually ornamented priests.

Having instilled fear, Ahuitzotl would then display a lighter hand, plying visiting warlords with flowers and gifts and tobacco at his palace. The emperor enjoyed entertaining—"in his house the music never ceased, day or night," according to one text from the era—but his yen for lavish ceremonies, coupled with his many wives and children, took its toll on Tenochtitlan's budget. The list of tribute goods supplied by the conquered provinces and enumerated by the 16th-century friar and chronicler Diego Durán reads like ad copy for Tiffany & Co.: "gold, jewels, ornaments, fine feathers, precious stones…countless articles of clothing and many adornments." The banquets must have been sumptuous, with "an amazing quantity of cacao, chiles, pumpkin seeds, all kinds of fruit, fowls and game." But it was never enough. More conquests would be ordered, along with measures to demonstrate the empire's power—as when Ahuitzotl avenged the killings of several merchants in 1497 by ordering warriors into the offending villages to slay 2,000 for every dead merchant.

More than any ruler before him, Ahuitzotl expanded the empire's reach southward, sealed off trade from the powerful Tarascans to the west, and tightened the reins on all the subjugated territories. "He was more forceful, more brutal," says archaeologist Raúl Arana. "When people didn't want to pay tribute, he sent in the military. With Ahuitzotl, the Aztec went to the maximum expression of everything. And perhaps it was too much. All empires have a limit."

The Mexica people lost their great empire builder at the pinnacle of their dominance. In 1502—10-Rabbit—Ahuitzotl perished, supposedly from a blow to the head while escaping his palace during a flood. The flood was caused by a hastily built aqueduct project Ahuitzotl had initiated to harness the springs flowing out of neighboring Coyoacan. The town's ruler had warned Ahuitzotl about the spring's highly irregular flows. The emperor had responded by putting the ruler to death. At Ahuitzotl's funeral, 200 of his slaves were selected as his companions for the hereafter. Outfitted in fine garments and carrying provisions for the journey, the slaves were led to the Templo Mayor, where their hearts were torn out and their bodies cast onto a funeral pyre. Their remains, and those of their master, were said to be buried in front of the Templo Mayor.

THAT VERY SPOT is where the Tlaltecuhtli monolith and the Aristo-Canine were discovered. López Luján's team has excavated other offerings in the immediate vicinity. One was found underneath a Tuscan-style mansion built for one of Cortés's soldiers. Another was discovered several feet under the large stone slab. In both cases López Luján knew where to look by tracing a complicated series of east-west axes, or "imaginary lines," on a map of the site. "There's always this repetitive symmetry," says López Luján. "It was like an obsession with them."

The archaeological team's work is slow and unglamorous. Some of this is due to the challenges of any urban excavation: obtaining permits and circumnavigating sewer and subway lines; avoiding underground telephone, fiber optic, and electric cables; and maintaining security for an archaeological area that lies within one of the world's most alluring pedestrian zones. But as much as anything else, López Luján's crew labors painstakingly because the exactitude of the Aztec requires no less. Standing over a pit where, in May 2007, his team unearthed an offering box no bigger than a footlocker, he says, "It took 15 months for us to go through that entire offering. In that small space, it had ten layers and over 5,000 objects. The concentration, the richness, is incredible.

"It looks random, but it's not," López Luján continues. "Everything has a cosmic significance. The challenge for us is to discover the logic and the spatial distribution patterns. When Leopoldo Batres worked here [during the turn of the previous century], he was interested in the objects themselves. They were archaeological trophies to him. What we've discovered in the 32 years we've been working here is that the objects aren't so important by themselves but by their connection in space."

Every finding is a huge boon for Mexico since so many fine artifacts were seized by the conquistadores and brought back to Spain, where they have been dispersed throughout Europe. Beyond their aesthetic value, the new discoveries highlight the Aztec's attention to detail—a preoccupation owing to the high stakes involved. For the Aztec, the appeasement of the gods—and thus the world's survival—depended on an ever growing, ever demanding empire that ultimately could not be sustained. As Carrasco says, "The irony of empire is that you push to the periphery and you push too far, until *you* become the periphery. You're so far from home that you can't support your warriors with food and transport and you can't protect your merchants. The empire becomes too expensive. And the Aztec couldn't manage it."

TEN YEARS BEFORE THE SPANIARDS arrived, Ahuitzotl's successor, Moctezuma II, was apparently plagued by visions and portents. Despite having continued his predecessor's expansionist ways, despite his great power and his gold and turquoise diadem and his 19 children and his zoo crammed with exotic animals and "dwarfs and albinos and hunchbacks"—despite all of this, the ninth Aztec ruler was beset by his own cosmic insecurity. In 1509, according to one codex, "a bad omen appeared in the sky. It was like a flaming ear of corn…it seemed to bleed fire, drop by drop, like a wound in the sky."

Moctezuma's worries were justified. "There were more than 50,000 indigenous warriors revolting, wanting to keep their goods and wanting the Aztec attacks to stop in their community," says Carrasco. Absent this appetite for an uprising, the 500 Spaniards who docked at Veracruz in the spring of 1519, even with their guns and cannon and horses, would have been no match for the Aztec armies.

Instead, Cortés's contingent arrived in Tenochtitlan on the eighth of November escorted by thousands of Tlaxcalan and allied warriors. As awed as the Spaniards were by the spectacle of this gleaming city on a lake—"some of the soldiers even asked whether the things that we saw were not a dream," one eyewitness recalled—they were not daunted by their host's prowess. Rather, it was Moctezuma who seemed unsure of himself. According to Mesoamerican legend, the great bearded deity Quetzalcoatl—banished after committing incest with his sister—would one day return by water to restore his lordship.

THE APPEASEMENT OF THE GODS DEPENDED ON AN EVER GROWING EMPIRE THAT COULD NOT BE SUSTAINED.

This notion was not lost on Moctezuma, who presented Cortés with "the treasure of Quetzalcoatl," a head-to-toe costuming topped off with "a serpent mask inlaid with turquoise."

But was Moctezuma really interpreting the Spaniard as the second coming of the feathered-serpent god, as has long been believed? Or was he cunningly outfitting Cortés in the godly garment of the soon-to-be sacrificed? The gesture was a final Aztec ambiguity. Thereafter, the facts are unassailable. The streets of Tenochtitlan ran red, and in 1521 an empire was buried.

"We're persuaded that sooner or later we'll find Ahuitzotl's tomb," says López Luján. "We're digging deeper and deeper." But no matter how deep the archaeologist digs, he will never unearth the core of the Aztec mystique. It will continue to occupy modern Mexico's psyche—there to be felt if not seen, at once primitive and majestic, summoning from ordinary mortals the power to turn swamps into kingdoms. □

Red crabs migrate
from forest to sea
on Australia's
Christmas Island.

NAT GEO CHANNEL **On the Move** This month the
National Geographic Channel presents *Great Migrations,* a
seven-part, global television event with unprecedented footage
of millions of animals making their instinctive treks in the name
of survival. Three years in the making, this program takes viewers
across the globe, intimately capturing the often harrowing
migrations of wildebeests, walruses, red crabs (above), and more.
Then it takes us behind the scenes to see the advanced technology required to capture this spectacular, high-definition show
of wildlife. Catch the first episode on November 7 at 8 p.m.

SPECIAL ISSUE **Sacred Journeys** What is it about
a place that compels us to travel there for spiritual sustenance?
From Mecca to Vatican City, destinations the world over draw
throngs of people seeking religious fulfillment. Yet for many
others a hike to Mount Fuji or a walk in the woods also offers

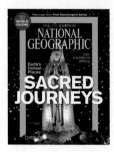

a powerful experience—and a holiness
of its own. Explore some of Earth's most
fascinating and important spiritual sites
in *Sacred Journeys,* featuring a map of
major pilgrimages and places and an
essay by *National Geographic's* senior
editor Don Belt. This new *National
Geographic* special issue is available
in bookstores November 2 or at
ngm.com/sacred-journeys ($10.99).

Society Updates

NG BOOKS
Brilliantly illustrated with
more than 250 color photographs, *Great Migrations* is
the essential companion
to the television series of the
same name. This book will
captivate animal lovers and
environmentalists alike with
its in-depth coverage of the
never-before-seen wildlife
behavior and stories show-
cased in the groundbreaking
documentary. Other highlights
include archival images and
unforgettable film stills. Look
for *Great Migrations* in bookstores in mid-October ($35).

GeoPuzzle Answers

SUBSCRIBE TO NATIONAL GEOGRAPHIC KIDS MAGAZINE FOR ONLY £12*

NATIONAL GEOGRAPHIC KIDS is an exciting and interactive magazine for children, which makes learning fun. Every month, readers will go on a new adventure – exploring the wonders of the natural world, getting up close with exotic wildlife, and discovering different cultures. Plus, they can test their knowledge with fun quizzes and puzzles, and get creative with exciting things to make and do. NATIONAL GEOGRAPHIC KIDS is everything an inquisitive young mind needs. **Let's get kids excited about their world!**

More reasons to subscribe today...

Free delivery each month
Exclusive subscriber competitions
NG KIDS gift card for you to send
A saving of over 35%

A fantastic birthday and Christmas gift

NATIONAL GEOGRAPHIC

Kids

THREE EASY WAYS TO SUBSCRIBE...

1 Fill in the coupon on the right and send to: NATIONAL GEOGRAPHIC KIDS, PO BOX 326, Sittingbourne, Kent ME9 8FA

2 Go to ngkids.co.uk or contact us by email at ngkids@servicehelpline.co.uk

3 Call our subscription hotline on 0844 322 1213†

Please quote promotion code NGK118

*Payment by Direct Debit for six issues – full price is £19.20 for six issues.

†Charged at 5p per minute from a landline.

BEST BUY **Yes!** Send **six** monthly issues of NG KIDS for only £12, paid by direct debit ☐ to me ☐ as a gift

DIRECT Debit 599674 **Instruction to your bank or building society to pay by direct debit**

To the manager [bank name]

Address

Post code

Name[s] of account holder[s]

Instructions to your bank or building society to pay direct debit
Please pay GalleonCI Ltd direct debits from the account detailed in this instruction, subject to the safeguards assured by The Direct Debit Guarantee. I understand that this instruction may remain with GalleonCI Ltd and, if so, details may be passed electronically to my bank / building society.

Branch sort code ☐☐ ☐☐ ☐☐

Bank / building society account number ☐☐☐☐☐☐☐☐

Signature[s]

Date

Yes! Send **six** monthly issues of NG KIDS for only £14, paid by credit / debit card or cheque ☐ to me ☐ as a gift

YOUR CREDIT / DEBIT CARD DETAILS
Please charge my debit card ☐ Visa Delta
Please charge my credit card ☐ Visa ☐ MasterCard
☐ American Express

Card number

Expiry date

Name as appears on card

Signature

TERMS & CONDITIONS This offer is available for subscriptions within the British Isles only (excluding BFPO addresses). All orders will be acknowledged and you will be advised of the commencement issue within 14 days. This offer cannot be used in conjunction with any other Galleonci Ltd, National Geographic or Attic Media Network Ltd subscription promotion and closes 31 March 2011. Initial six-month non-refundable contract applies. Unless written notice is given before the end of the initial term, the subscription will continue as a rolling six-month non-refundable contract. The full UK subscription rate is £38.40 for 12 issues. For subscription enquiries, please call 0844 322 1213 (if calling from outside the UK please call +44 1795 412847). By supplying your email address / mail address, you are happy to receive products and services via email / post from, or in association with, Attic Media Network Ltd / National Geographic. Please tick if you do not want to receive offers from us ☐ or third parties ☐.
For our data policy, see subscribeonline.co.uk/ngkids

MY DETAILS (please fill in even if subscription is a gift)
Title   Surname
Forename
Address

Post code   Date of birth
Telephone
Email address

The subscription is a gift. Please send copies to:
Title   Surname
Forename
Address

Post code   Date of birth
Telephone
Email address

Modern Mermaids A Japanese ama goes overboard in
search of shellfish in the 1930s. For centuries these female free divers
worked the country's coasts without much clothing, but that changed:
"Except for a few older women, the ama of Hekura no longer dive
semi-naked," wrote Luis Marden after visiting one group of divers. His
July 1971 *Geographic* story, "Ama, Sea Nymphs of Japan," goes on to
say, "The girls wore black leotards. Most others wore all-enveloping
suits of black neoprene, the diver's wetsuit."

There aren't many ama left in Japan. Most who remain are middle-
aged or older; divers sometimes work into their 80s. Today few young
women care to take the plunge. —*Margaret G. Zackowitz*

↖ **Flashback Archive** Find all the photos at **ngm.com.**

NATIONAL GEOGRAPHIC (ISSN 0027-9358) PUBLISHED MONTHLY BY THE NATIONAL GEOGRAPHIC SOCIETY, 1145 17TH ST. NW, WASHINGTON, DC 20036. ONE YEAR MEMBERSHIP: $34.00 U.S. DELIVERY, $38.00 TO CANADA, $49.50 TO INTERNATIONAL ADDRESSES. SINGLE ISSUE: $7.00 U.S. DELIVERY, $10.00 CANADA, $15.00 INTERNATIONAL. (ALL PRICES IN U.S. FUNDS; INCLUDES SHIPPING AND HAN-
DLING.) PERIODICALS POSTAGE PAID AT WASHINGTON, DC, AND ADDITIONAL MAILING OFFICES. POSTMASTER: SEND ADDRESS CHANGES TO NATIONAL GEOGRAPHIC, PO BOX 63002, TAMPA, FL 33663. IN
CANADA, AGREEMENT NUMBER 40063649, RETURN UNDELIVERABLE ADDRESSES TO NATIONAL GEOGRAPHIC, PO BOX 4412 STN. A, TORONTO, ONTARIO M5W 3W2. UNITED KINGDOM NEWSSTAND PRICE
£4.99. REPR. EN FRANCE: EMD FRANCE SA, BP 1029, 59011 LILLE CEDEX; TEL. 320.300.302; CPPAP 0710U89037; DIRECTEUR PUBLICATION: D. TASSINARI DIR. RESP. ITALY; RAPP IMD SRL, VIA G. DA VELATE
11, 20162 MILANO; AUT. TRIB. MI 258 26/5/84 POSTE ITALIANE SPA; SPED. ABB. POST. DL 353/2003 (CONV L.27/02/2004 N.46) ART 1 C. 1 DCB MILANO STAMPA QUAD/GRAPHICS, MARTINSBURG, WV 25401.
MEMBERS: IF THE POSTAL SERVICE ALERTS US THAT YOUR MAGAZINE IS UNDELIVERABLE, WE HAVE NO FURTHER OBLIGATION UNLESS WE RECEIVE A CORRECTED ADDRESS WITHIN TWO YEARS.

Move as millions.
Survive as one.

Migration is one of the greatest spectacles nature orchestrates—a dramatic, dangerous, and crucial endeavour for countless species.
All over the world, by land, air, and sea, millions of animals undertake epic journeys each year—some as long as 44,000 miles.

Explore the science and wonder of migration in *Great Migrations*, the official companion book to the National Geographic Channel global television event starting on 7th November. The all-National Geographic television team spent two and a half years in the field, traveling 420,000 miles in 20 countries and all seven continents to track some of nature's most amazing animals. Filled with action, fascination, and beauty, *Great Migrations* showcases both the grandeur and the challenge of these amazing journeys, set against the magnificent backdrop of the natural world. Monarch butterflies, red crabs, whale sharks, rockhopper penguins, proboscis monkeys, and more—their stories are presented with compelling narrative and stunning imagery.

Great Migrations, £19.99, 9781426206443
Available from all good book retailers **amazon**.co.uk

NATIONAL GEOGRAPHIC

As the party started swinging, it was clear who had taken their Jointace®...

Flexibility

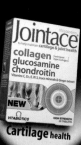

Cartilage health

Joint Mobility

MAX support

Gel

Fizz

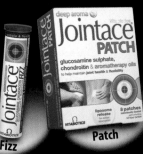

Patch

"Healthy joints are an essential part of an active life. The Jointace® range has been specially formulated to deliver targeted, premium nutritional care for those who really care about their joints. Every advanced Jointace® product has been produced to high pharmaceutical quality standards to ensure you receive exceptional joint support."

Prof. A. H. Beckett
OBE, PhD, DSc
Professor Emeritus,
University of London

Jointace
Vitabiotics
helping to keep you **supple & flexible**

From Boots, Superdrug, supermarkets, Lloydspharmacy, chemists, Holland & Barrett, GNC, health stores & www.jointace.com

THE QUEEN'S AWARDS FOR ENTERPRISE 2008

Britain's leading supplements for specific life stages

Ω **VITABIOTICS**
WHERE NATURE MEETS SCIENCE

Learning a language?
Consider it child's play.

Think about how you learnt your native language as a child. The world was your classroom, but there were no lessons. You were an active participant in the process of learning, but it all seemed like fun and games. **Like child's play.**

That's the secret to Rosetta Stone®. We unlock your brain's natural ability to learn a language. You'll learn through engaging, interactive activities that encourage you to think in the new language. And just like a child, you won't memorise or translate. You'll have fun as you progress, and you'll find it easy to achieve your language learning goals.

OVER 30 LANGUAGES AVAILABLE

UP TO £50 OFF
PLUS FREE DELIVERY

Quote 'nat10'

Free call 0800 005 1194
RosettaStone.co.uk/nat10

RosettaStone®

AUTUMN SALE OFFER
UP TO
50%OFF
on selected showers

❝ I said goodbye to bathing difficulties when I had my new easy entry shower installed by Bathing Solutions. ❞

The Elegance

Aquarius Wet Room

The Finesse

The Elegance our most popular easy entry shower

Aquarius Wet Room the ultimate easy entry shower

The Finesse stylish design with the convenience of a no-door easy entry shower

bathing solutions
making bathing a pleasure again

For a free copy of our 28 page brochure call free now on

0800 783 1912

PLEASE QUOTE OFFER
REFERENCE NGSRO0

Features
- Low threshold trays
- Easy clean wall panels
- No tiles and messy grout to clean
- Anti-slip shower tray
- Grab rails for extra support
- Fold-up seat for added comfort
- Fully guaranteed

Please send me a brochure on your range of easy entry showers and walk-in baths.

NGSRO0

Name_____

Tel No._____

Address_____

_____ Postcode _____

bathing solutions
making bathing a pleasure again

Bathing Solutions and other group companies may send you information and offers in the future. Please tick box if you do not wish to receive information from us ☐ or third parties ☐ in the future.

Post coupon to: Bathing Solutions, FREEPOST SWC3136, Ledbury, HR8 2ZZ

Odd-ysseys

Puzzle by Cathy Allis

Why did the pronghorn (left) cross the road? To get to the next stage in their migration. The amazing journeys of all sorts of animals are grist for the tinted answers. To bone up on migratory facts, see the article on page 28.

DOWN

1 Former fast flier to JFK
2 Goals on greens
3 Tandoor, e.g.
4 Russian form of the saint aka Santa
5 Ten to the hundredth power
6 Mix metaphors, say
7 Org. that "tracks" Santa
8 Prenatal "nurseries"
9 Loud and overbearing
10 He's hardly a teetotaler
11 Like some drones
12 Rudimentary
13 Radiate, as confidence
18 Does some back-and-forth switching
22 Shark type
24 Bagged launch
25 Infield protector
26 One working in a sub way
27 Blue hue
28 Checkout-aisle assortment
32 Suffix akin to "-ian"
33 Where suds are made and served
35 Mideast sultanate
36 It gets reefed
37 Award for *Bye Bye Birdie*
39 Skinniness exemplar
40 Superstar
43 __ crier
45 Thoroughbred grandfather of Seabiscuit
47 Surgically tie
49 Actress Mason in *The Goodbye Girl*
50 Mating game
51 Scamp
52 Bakery lure
53 Subject of SALT I and II
54 Like nu
58 Did a round
59 Sandusky's lake
61 Wee bit
62 Fashion designer's monogram
63 Deface

ACROSS

1 Marine animal that's no square
7 Little lumps
11 Mount Rushmore prez
14 Rescuer
15 Oaxacan "other"
16 Roman goddess of peace
17 Choice an arctic tern might face when offered a mid-migration herring
19 Terre Haute sch.
20 Make out, in Liverpool
21 Hydrodynamic duo
22 Inn need
23 With 50 Across, prairie rattlers' migration scheme?

26 Language of Manila
29 Schmooze
30 Prefix with lateral
31 Smooth-talking
34 Passerine's perch
38 Not talking
39 Chinook salmon's migration to its birthplace for egg laying?
41 Long March leader
42 Capellini or cannelloni
44 Brazil nut, botanically
45 Chief
46 Enemy in this year's Gulf "war"?
48 Feminine
50 See 23 Across

55 Cape of Chile
56 Spiritual adviser
57 Its hips may be in tea
60 It's behind hubris
61 Overwhelm like monarch butterflies during their migration?
64 Abacus calculation
65 Suit to __
66 Grammy winner Twain
67 Salmon's first migration destination
68 Place for a modesty panel
69 Swans vis-à-vis swallows

Answers in Inside Geographic

PRESENTING THE NATIONAL GEOGRAPHIC PHOTOGRAPHY CONTEST

Enter to win $10,000 and have your photo published in *National Geographic* magazine. As a leader in capturing our world through brilliant imagery, *National Geographic* sets the standard for photographic excellence. Now you can share your vision of the world through your own photography.

Submit your entry online in any of these three categories:

PEOPLE · PLACES · NATURE

Hurry, contest ends November 30, 2010.

For more details, rules, and information on how you can enter today, visit ngphotocontest.com.

150 YEARS

GREEN CROSS International

A PARTNERSHIP TO BENEFIT ENVIRONMENTAL CHARITIES

Leonardo DiCaprio and TAG Heuer have joined forces to contribute to Green Cross International initiatives. To learn more please visit www.tagheuer.com

HISTORY BEGINS EVERY MORNING

TAGHeuer

SWISS AVANT-GARDE SINCE 1860

Carrera Series